Charge through your exams with CGP!

There's a lot to learn in Edexcel Grade 9-1 International GCSE Physics —
you'll need to be on top of your game when the exams come around.

Luckily, this fantastic CGP book is bursting with realistic exam-style
questions for the whole course*, plus two complete practice exam papers.
Everything you need to make sure you're 100% ready for the real thing!

We've even included step-by-step answers at the back of the book,
so it's easy to find out how well you're getting on.

* It's great for the Physics parts of the Edexcel International GCSE Science Double Award too.

CGP — still the best! ☺

Our sole aim here at CGP is to produce the highest quality books —
carefully written, immaculately presented and dangerously close to being funny.

Then we work our socks off to get them out to you
— at the cheapest possible prices.

Contents

Use the tick boxes to check off the topics you've completed.

Published by CGP

Editors:
Sarah Armstrong, Duncan Lindsay, Andy Park and Charlotte Whiteley.

With thanks to Ian Francis, Lucy Johnson, Simon Little, Glenn Rogers and Frances Rooney for the proofreading.

With thanks to Ana Pungartnik for the copyright research.

ISBN: 978 1 78294 688 5

Data used to construct stopping distance diagram on page 104 from the Highway Code.
Contains public sector information licensed under the Open Government Licence v3.0.
http://www.nationalarchives.gov.uk/doc/open-government-licence/version/3/

Graph on page 123 contains public sector information licensed under the Open Government Licence v3.0.
http://www.nationalarchives.gov.uk/doc/open-government-licence/version/3/

Clipart from Corel®
Printed by Elanders Ltd, Newcastle upon Tyne

Based on the classic CGP style created by Richard Parsons.

How To Use This Book

- Hold the book <u>upright</u>, approximately <u>50 cm</u> from your face, ensuring that the text looks like <u>this</u>, not this. Alternatively, place the book on a <u>horizontal</u> surface (e.g. a table or desk) and sit adjacent to the book, at a distance which doesn't make the text too small to read.

- In case of emergency, press the two halves of the book together <u>firmly</u> in order to close.

- Before attempting to use this book, familiarise yourself with the following <u>safety information</u>:

The questions are arranged into topics, so you can get exam practice on exactly the bit of your course that you want.

Some questions are multiple choice and you'll need to answer by putting a cross in a box, like this: X

There are answer lines for you to write your answers on. For calculation questions, there's also space for you to do your working.

There are boxes to show you which questions test Paper 2 material.

These are stamps to show you which questions are about the practicals you could be tested on in the exams. If the stamp is by the page title, the whole page is about that practical.

You're told how many marks each question part is worth, and then the total for the whole question.

Use the answers at the back of the book to mark each page. Then you can find your score out of the total for the topic. If you're not doing the Paper 2 questions, the total score for some topics will be lower.

Exam Practice Tips give you hints to help with answering exam questions.

Tick the box that matches how confident you feel with the questions in each topic. This should help show you where you need to focus your revision.

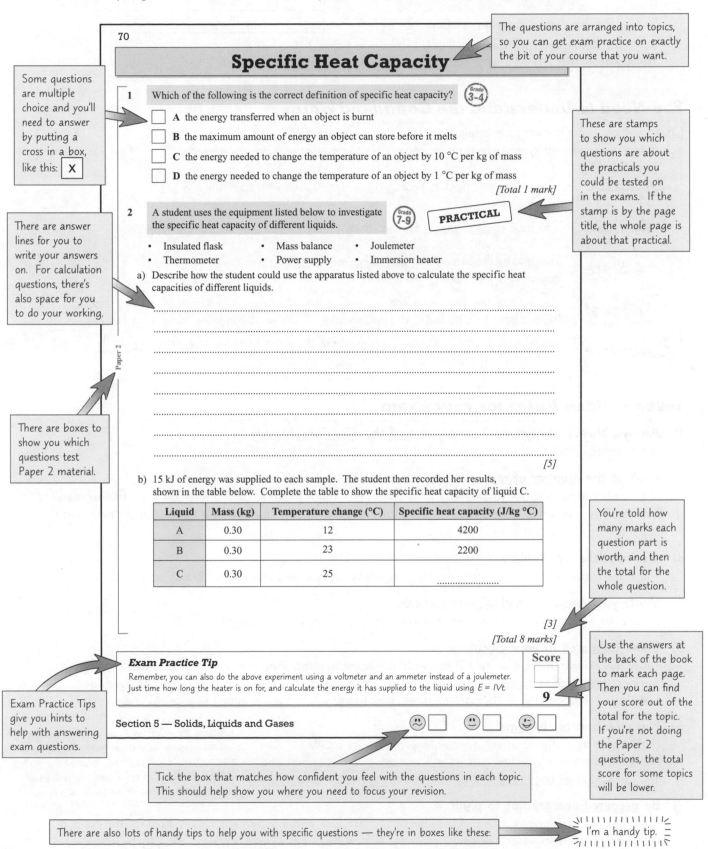

70

Specific Heat Capacity

1 Which of the following is the correct definition of specific heat capacity? (Grade 3-4)

☐ **A** the energy transferred when an object is burnt

☐ **B** the maximum amount of energy an object can store before it melts

☐ **C** the energy needed to change the temperature of an object by 10 °C per kg of mass

☐ **D** the energy needed to change the temperature of an object by 1 °C per kg of mass

[Total 1 mark]

2 A student uses the equipment listed below to investigate the specific heat capacity of different liquids. (Grade 7-9) PRACTICAL

- Insulated flask   • Mass balance   • Joulemeter
- Thermometer   • Power supply   • Immersion heater

a) Describe how the student could use the apparatus listed above to calculate the specific heat capacities of different liquids.

....

....

....

....

....

....

....

[5]

b) 15 kJ of energy was supplied to each sample. The student then recorded her results, shown in the table below. Complete the table to show the specific heat capacity of liquid C.

Liquid	Mass (kg)	Temperature change (°C)	Specific heat capacity (J/kg °C)
A	0.30	12	4200
B	0.30	23	2200
C	0.30	25	....

[3]

[Total 8 marks]

Exam Practice Tip

Remember, you can also do the above experiment using a voltmeter and an ammeter instead of a joulemeter. Just time how long the heater is on for, and calculate the energy it has supplied to the liquid using $E = IVt$.

Score

☐ / 9

Section 5 — Solids, Liquids and Gases   ☹ ☐   😐 ☐   😊 ☐

Paper 2

There are also lots of handy tips to help you with specific questions — they're in boxes like these: → I'm a handy tip.

Exam Tips

Before you get cracking on some exam practice, here's some handy information and some tips to help you in the exams.

Edexcel International GCSE Exam Stuff

1) For the Edexcel International GCSE in Physics, you'll sit two exam papers at the end of your course.

2) If you're doing the Edexcel International GCSE Science Double Award, you won't sit Paper 2.

Paper	Time	No. of marks
1	2 hours	110
2	1 hr 15 mins	70

3) Some material in the specification will only be tested in Paper 2. The questions that cover Paper 2 material in this book are marked with a Paper 2 box.

You Need to Understand the Command Words

Command words are the words in a question that tell you what to do.
If you don't know what they mean, you might not be able to answer the questions properly.

Describe — This means you need to recall facts or write about what something is like.

Explain — You have to give reasons for something or say why or how something happens.

State — This means the same thing as 'Name...' or 'Give...'.
You usually just have to give a short definition or an example of something.

Suggest — You need to use your knowledge to work out the answer. It'll often be something you haven't been taught, but you should be able to use what you know to figure it out.

Calculate — This means you'll have to use numbers from the question to work something out.
You'll probably have to get your calculator out.

Seven Golden Rules for your Exam

1) **Always, always, always make sure you read the question properly.**
   For example, if the question asks you to give your answer in mm, don't give it in cm.

2) **Look at the number of marks a question is worth.**
   The number of marks gives you a pretty good clue of how much to write. So if a question is worth four marks, make sure you write four decent points. And there's no point writing an essay for a question that's only worth one mark — it's just a waste of your time.

3) **Use specialist vocabulary.**
   You know the words I mean — the sciencey ones, like conduction and convection. Examiners love them.

4) **Write your answers as clearly as you can.**
   If the examiner can't read your answer you won't get any marks, even if it's right.

5) **Show each step in your calculations.**
   You're less likely to make a mistake if you write things out in steps. And even if your final answer's wrong, you'll probably pick up some marks if the examiner can see that your method is right. You also need to make sure you're working in the right units — check before you put any numbers in your calculator.

6) **Pay attention to the time.**
   Don't spend ages staring at the question paper. If you're totally, hopelessly stuck on a question, just leave it and move on to the next one. You can always go back to it at the end if you've got enough time.

   Obeying these Golden Rules will help you get as many marks as you can in the exams — but they're no use if you haven't learnt the stuff in the first place. So make sure you revise well and do as many practice questions as you can.

7) **Be prepared and try not to panic.**
   Exam day can give anyone a case of the jitters. So make sure you've got everything you need for the exam (pen, spare pen, pencil, ruler, calculator) ready the night before. Eat a good breakfast. And try to relax...

Velocity and Acceleration

1 A cyclist travels 1500 m from his house to his local shops in 300 seconds. *(Grade 4-6)*

a) State the equation linking average speed, distance moved and time taken.

....
[1]

b) Calculate the cyclist's average speed during his journey.

Average speed = ... m/s
[2]

c) On the return home, the cyclist accelerates from 2.0 m/s with a steady acceleration of 2.4 m/s².
Calculate the time it takes the cyclist to reach a speed of 10 m/s.

Time = ... s
[3]

[Total 6 marks]

2 A coin is rolled in a straight line along a balcony edge at a steady speed of 0.46 m/s. *(Grade 4-6)*

a) Calculate how far the coin rolls in 2.4 s.

Distance = ... m
[3]

b) Another coin is dropped from the balcony. It accelerates from rest and hits the ground after
8.0 seconds at a speed of 78.4 m/s. Calculate the acceleration of the coin during its fall.

Acceleration = ... m/s²
[2]

[Total 5 marks]

3   A model car company produces battery-powered model cars. At its maximum acceleration, their latest model accelerates from rest to its top speed in 3.5 s.

a)   While the car is travelling at its top speed, it covers 180 m in 9.0 s. Calculate the car's maximum acceleration.

Acceleration = ... m/s²

[3]

b)   Calculate how fast the car would be moving if it accelerated from rest for 1.5 seconds with its maximum acceleration.

Velocity = ... m/s

[3]

[Total 6 marks]

4   A tractor ploughing a field accelerates at 2 m/s² for 10 metres, after which its velocity is 7 m/s.

a)   Calculate the tractor's velocity before it started accelerating.

Velocity = ... m/s

[3]

b)   As the tractor approaches the end of the field, it turns at a constant speed until it's facing the opposite direction. State whether the tractor accelerates during this time and explain your answer.

....

....

[1]

[Total 4 marks]

Exam Practice Tip

Acceleration and velocity questions are exam favourites so make sure you're happy with them. If you're given one of these questions and you're not sure which equation to use, try listing the quantities that you've been given and the one you need to work out. Write the equations next to it and see which one fits them best.

Score

21

Section 1 — Forces and Motion

Distance-Time and Velocity-Time Graphs

1 A student walks to football training but finds she has left her boots at home. She turns around and walks back home, where she spends 50 seconds looking for the boots. Below is a distance-time graph for her journey.

a) Use the graph to find the time it took for the student to walk to training.

Time = ... s
[1]

b) State whether the student walked to training at a steady speed. Explain how you know.

....

....

....

....

....
[2]

c) Use the graph to calculate the student's speed as she walked to football training.

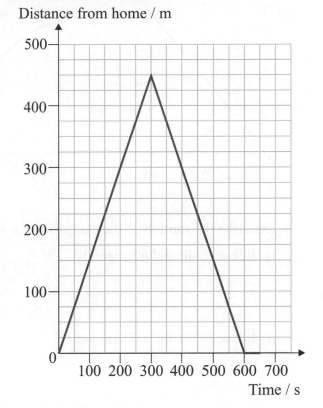

Distance from home / m

Time / s

Average speed = ... m/s
[2]

d) The student returns home in a car after training. At the start of the journey, the car accelerates at a constant rate for 10 s. It then travels at a constant speed for a further 30 s.

On the axes below, sketch a velocity-time graph to show the motion of the car during this time.

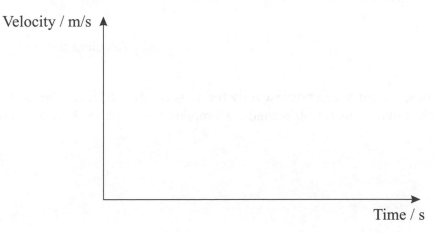

Velocity / m/s

Time / s

[3]
[Total 8 marks]

2 The diagram shows a velocity-time graph for a car during a section of a journey.

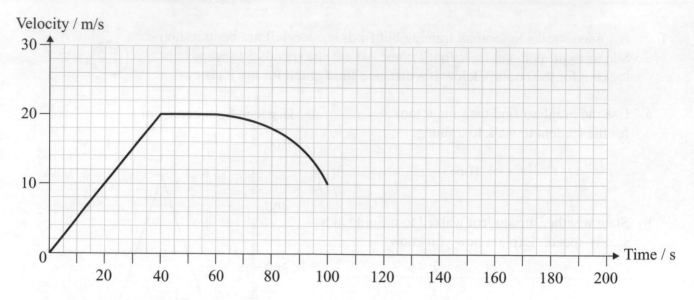

a) Describe the motion of the car during the following parts of the journey.

   i) Between 40 and 60 seconds.

   ....
   [1]

   ii) Between 60 and 100 seconds.

   ....
   [1]

b) Use the graph to calculate the distance travelled by the car between 40 and 60 seconds.

   Distance travelled = ... m
   [3]

c) Use the graph to calculate the acceleration of the car between 0 and 40 seconds.

   Acceleration = ... m/s²
   [3]

d) After 100 seconds, the car accelerates steadily for 40 seconds until it reaches a steady velocity
   of 30 m/s, which it maintains for 60 seconds. Complete the graph to show this motion.
   [2]
   [Total 10 marks]

Score:

18

Mass, Weight and Gravity

1   A student is measuring gravitational field strength, *g*, in a classroom experiment. He takes an object with a mass of 2.0 kg and suspends it from a newton meter held in his hand. He takes multiple readings of the object's weight and calculates an average value of 19.6 N.

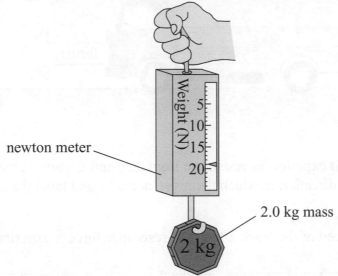

newton meter

Weight (N)

2.0 kg mass

a) i) State the equation linking weight, mass and gravitational field strength.

....

[1]

ii) Calculate the gravitational field strength in the student's classroom and give the unit.

Gravitational field strength = ... unit ....

[3]

b) The Moon's gravity is weaker than the Earth's. State how the student's measurement of the object's weight would differ if he performed the same experiment on the Moon. Explain your answer.

....

....

....

[2]

[Total 6 marks]

Exam Practice Tip

At first it's a little tricky to get your head around the fact that mass and weight are two different things — particularly because what we've been told all our lives is our 'weight' is actually our mass. To clear things up, just try and remember that weight is a force, measured in newtons. It's pretty simple after that.

Score

6

Forces and Friction

1   The diagram below shows a truck moving forwards at a steady speed. The thrust (driving force) acting on the truck is shown.

thrust

a) i) As the truck moves, it experiences resistance from drag and friction. Draw an arrow on the diagram to show the direction in which the resistance acts, and label the arrow.

[1]

ii) Describe how the speed of the truck affects the resistance force it experiences.

....

....

[1]

b) Draw and label an arrow on the diagram to show **one** more force that acts on the truck.

[2]

[Total 4 marks]

2   A plane is flying at a constant speed and altitude. **Grade 6-7**

a) Give the name of the force that pulls the plane straight downwards towards the Earth.

....

[1]

b) The plane deploys a parachute to slow down when it lands, as shown below. Explain why the parachute slows the plane down.

....

....

....

[2]

[Total 3 marks]

Score: [   ]

7

Investigating Motion

1   A student wants to carry out an experiment to investigate the motion of a trolley down a ramp. Her textbook suggests setting up her apparatus as shown in the diagram.

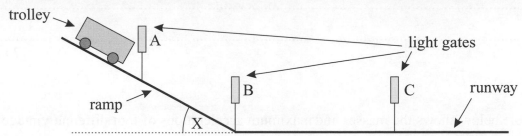

a) Describe how she could use this apparatus to find the acceleration of the trolley down the ramp.

....

....

....

....

....

....

....

....

....

....

[6]

b) The student decides to investigate how the distance the car travels down the ramp and the angle of the ramp (X) affect the car's speed at the bottom of the ramp. She changes both the angle of the ramp and the distance of the car along the ramp each time she repeats the experiment, and uses light gates to measure the car's speed at the bottom.

She concludes that as the angle of the ramp decreases, the speed of the car increases. Explain why she cannot conclude this from her data and suggest how this experiment can be improved.

....

....

....

....

[3]

[Total 9 marks]

Score: ☐
___
9

 ☐   ☐   ☺ ☐

The Three Laws of Motion

1 State Newton's third law. Grade 3-4

....

....

[Total 1 mark]

2 The table below shows the masses and maximum accelerations of four different vintage cars.

Car	Mass (kg)	Maximum acceleration (m/s²)
Disraeli 9000	....	5
Palmerston 6i	1560	0.7
Heath TT	950	3
Asquith 380	790	2

a) Show that the Heath TT has a greater maximum driving force than the Asquith 380.
   You may assume that all frictional forces are negligible.

[2]

b) The Disraeli 9000 has a maximum driving force of 4000 N. Use this information to complete the
   table above. You may assume that all frictional forces are negligible.

[2]

[Total 4 marks]

3 A camper van has a mass of 2500 kg. It is driven along a straight,
   level road at a constant speed of 90 kilometres per hour.

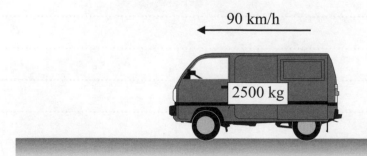

90 km/h

2500 kg

a) A headwind begins blowing with a force of 200 N, causing the van to slow down. Calculate the van's deceleration.

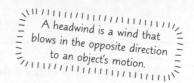

A headwind is a wind that blows in the opposite direction to an object's motion.

Deceleration = ... m/s^2

[2]

b) The van begins travelling at a steady speed before colliding with a stationary traffic cone that has a mass of 10 kg. The traffic cone accelerates at 29 m/s^2 in the direction of the van's motion.

i) Calculate the force applied to the traffic cone by the van.

Force = ... N

[2]

ii) State the size of the force applied by the cone to the van during the collision.

Remember Newton's third law of motion when you're answering this question.

Force = ... N

[1]

iii) Calculate the deceleration of the van during the collision.
Assume all of the force applied by the cone to the van causes the deceleration.

Deceleration = ... m/s^2

[2]

[Total 7 marks]

4 Two students have fitted their scooters with the same engine. Student A and his scooter have a combined mass of 127.5 kg and a maximum acceleration of 2.40 m/s^2. Student B has a maximum acceleration of 1.70 m/s^2 on her scooter.

Show that the combined mass of student B and her scooter is 180 kg.
You may assume that the frictional forces acting on each scooter are negligible.

[Total 4 marks]

Exam Practice Tip

Newton's laws are a very important bit of physics, so take the time to get to know them. Don't forget, an object doesn't need a resultant force on it to move — a moving object will continue travelling at a constant speed so long as the forces acting on it are balanced. A resultant force will cause the object to accelerate.

Score

16

Section 1 — Forces and Motion

Combining Forces

1 Most quantities can be divided into two groups: scalars and vectors. (Grade 3-4)

a) Describe the difference between a scalar and a vector quantity.

....

....
[2]

b) Which of the following is a **vector**?

☐ **A** speed   ☐ **B** time   ☐ **C** mass   ☐ **D** force
[1]

c) Which of the following is a **scalar**?

☐ **A** 14 kg   ☐ **B** 300 kN down   ☐ **C** 24 m/s west   ☐ **D** 1 m/s² up
[1]

[Total 4 marks]

2 The figure below shows two hot air balloons, labelled with the forces acting on them. (Grade 6-7)

Balloon A   ↑ 300 N
1700 N →
← 2000 N
300 N ⇒
↓ 800 N

Balloon B   ↑ y
← x
2000 N →
← 500 N
↓ 400 N

a) Calculate the resultant force acting on balloon A.

Force = ... N   direction ....
[2]

b) The resultant force acting on balloon B is zero.

i) Calculate the size of force y.

y = ... N
[1]

ii) Calculate the size of force x.

x = ... N
[1]

[Total 4 marks]

Score: ☐

8

Section 1 — Forces and Motion

Terminal Velocity

1   A flying squirrel has a membrane of skin, called a patagium, joining its wrists to its ankles on each side of its body. It opens the patagium when it jumps or falls from a tree.

Grade 6-7

a) Explain why a falling object reaches a terminal velocity.

....

....

....

....

[4]

b) A flying squirrel falls from a tall tree, reaching a terminal velocity of 8.5 m/s. Explain how the patagium affects the squirrel's terminal velocity.

....

[1]

c) Use the axes below to sketch a graph showing the squirrel's vertical velocity against time.

Velocity / m/s

8.5 –

→ Time

[2]

[Total 7 marks]

2   A student is studying the forces acting on objects falling at terminal velocity.

Grade 7-9

The student takes two balls of the same size but with different weights and drops them off a high balcony. Which of the two balls will have a lower terminal velocity? Explain your answer.

....

....

....

[Total 3 marks]

Score:

10

Section 1 — Forces and Motion

Hooke's Law

1   A student investigates how a spring extends when a force is applied to it.   PRACTICAL

His results are shown in the table below.

Force (N)	1.00	2.00	3.00	4.00	5.00	6.00	7.00	8.00	8.25
Extension (mm)	3	6	8	11	14	16	20	27	38

a) Plot these results on the axes below and draw a line of best fit.

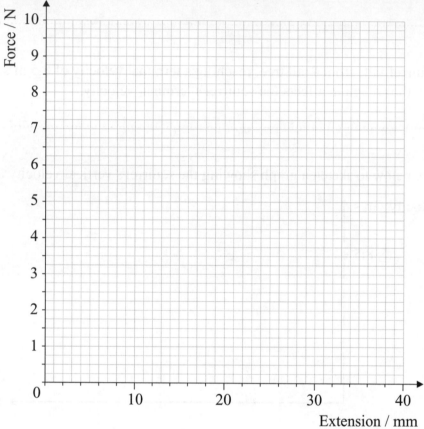

[3]

b) Describe the relationship between force and extension up to a force of 5 N.

....

[1]

c) An identical spring is pulled with a force of 7.5 N. The elastic limit of the spring is 7.2 N.
    State and explain whether or not the spring will return to its original shape.

....

....

[1]

[Total 5 marks]

Score: ⬜
___
5

Section 1 — Forces and Motion

 ⬜   ⬜   ☺ ⬜

Stopping Distances

1 The stopping distance of a car is the distance covered in the time between the driver first spotting a hazard and the car coming to a complete stop.

a) i) What name is given to the distance travelled by a car between the driver first spotting a hazard and the driver applying the brakes?

....

[1]

ii) Give **two** factors that can affect this distance.

1. ....

2. ....

[2]

b) i) What is meant by the **braking distance** of a car?

....

[1]

ii) Give **two** factors that can affect this distance.

1. ....

2. ....

[2]

[Total 6 marks]

2 A person is driving a car in heavy rain.

a) State and explain one way in which heavy rain can increase a car's stopping distance.

....

....

[2]

b) Suggest **one** way a driver can decrease their stopping distance if driving in heavy rain.

....

[1]

c) The driver sees a deer and stops the car. The car covers a distance of 37 m between the driver spotting the deer and the car coming to a stop. The braking distance of the car is 28 m. Calculate the thinking distance covered by the car.

Thinking distance = ... m

[2]

[Total 5 marks]

Score: ⬚

11

Momentum and Collisions

1   A 65 kg stuntperson jumps from a balcony onto an inflated airbag. Her speed is 14 m/s just before she hits the airbag. She is stopped in a period of 1.3 seconds (after which her momentum is zero).

a) i) State the equation linking momentum, mass and velocity.

....
[1]

ii) Calculate the momentum of the stuntperson just before she hits the airbag and give the unit.

Momentum = ... unit ....
[3]

b) i) State the equation linking force, change in momentum and time taken.

....
[1]

ii) Calculate the size of the average force acting on the stuntperson as she is stopped by the airbag.

Force = ... N
[2]
[Total 7 marks]

2   A skater with a mass of 60 kg is moving at 5.0 m/s. He skates past a bag and picks it up from the floor, causing him to slow down to 4.8 m/s.

Calculate the mass of the bag. Assume there are no frictional forces.

Mass = ... kg
[Total 5 marks]

3 In a demolition derby, cars drive around an arena and crash into each other.

a) One car has a mass of 650 kg and a velocity of 15 m/s.
   Calculate the momentum of the car.

Momentum = ... kg m/s

[2]

b) The car collides head-on with another car with a mass of 750 kg moving in the opposite direction.
   The two cars stick together. Calculate the combined velocity of the two cars immediately after
   the crash if the other car was travelling at 10 m/s before the collision.

Velocity = ... m/s

[4]

c) The cars have crumple zones at the front of the car that crumple on impact.
   Explain how a crumple zone reduces the forces acting on a driver during a collision.

....

....

....

[2]

[Total 8 marks]

Section 1 — Forces and Motion

4   Two fairground dodgems collide head-on. The mass of dodgem A and its
rider is 410 kg and the mass of dodgem B and its rider is 440 kg. Before
they collide, the dodgems are moving with the velocities shown below.

410 kg   440 kg

A   →   ←   B
        2.0 m/s   −1.1 m/s

a) i) Calculate the momentum of dodgem A before the collision.

Momentum of dodgem A before collision = ... kg m/s

[2]

ii) The momentum of dodgem B before the collision is −484 kg m/s.
Calculate the total momentum of the two dodgems before the collision.

Total momentum of dodgems before collision = ... kg m/s

[1]

b) The dodgems bounce off each other. After the collision, dodgem A has a velocity of −1.2 m/s
and dodgem B has a velocity v, as shown below.

←   A   B   →
−1.2 m/s v

i) State the total momentum of the two dodgems after the collision.

Total momentum of dodgems after collision = ... kg m/s

[1]

ii) Find the velocity v of dodgem B after the collision.

$v =$ .... m/s

[3]

[Total 7 marks]

Exam Practice Tip

Whenever you see a question about collisions there are two things of which you can be pretty sure — it's
going to involve momentum and it's going to involve a lot of rearrangement. Similarly, if there's a question
about car safety features, you can bet your bottom dollar it'll be about changes in momentum over time.

Score

27

Section 1 — Forces and Motion

Turning Effects and Centre of Gravity

1 State what is meant by an object's **centre of gravity**. *(Grade 3-4)*

....

[Total 1 mark]

2 A door has a horizontal door handle. To open the door, its handle needs to be rotated clockwise. *(Grade 6-7)*

a) State what is meant by the **moment** of a force.

....

[1]

b) Pictures A, B, C and D show equal forces being exerted on the handle.

| A | B | C | D |

pivot   force

State which picture shows the largest moment on the handle. Explain your answer.

....

....

....

[2]

c) A force of 45 N is exerted vertically downwards on the door handle at a distance of 0.1 m from the pivot. Calculate the moment about the pivot and give the unit.

Moment = ... unit ....

[3]

[Total 6 marks]

Exam Practice Tip

The important thing to remember with moments is that it's the **perpendicular** distance to the pivot that counts, so the direction in which the force acts really matters. If two forces are the same size and act at the same distance from the pivot, they won't produce the same moment if they're at different angles to each other.

Score

☐

─

7

Section 1 — Forces and Motion

Principle of Moments

1 The diagram shows three weights on a wooden plank, resting on a pivot. Weight A is 2 N and sits 20 cm to the left of the pivot. Weight B exerts an anticlockwise moment of 0.8 Nm. Assume the plank has no weight.

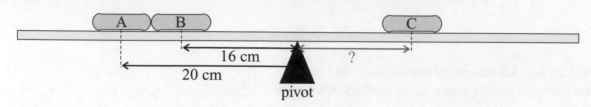

a) Calculate the anticlockwise moment exerted by weight A.

Weight A anticlockwise moment = ... Nm

[3]

b) The system is currently balanced. Weight C has a weight of 8 N.
Calculate the distance of weight C from the pivot.

Distance = ... m

[4]

[Total 7 marks]

2 A light plank is suspended horizontally by two ropes, one at either end, and a heavy box is placed on the plank in two different positions.

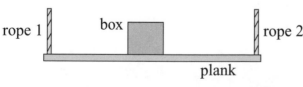

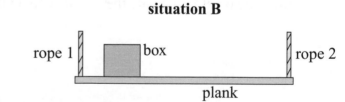

State in which situation rope 1 is applying more force to the plank. Explain your answer.

....

....

....

[Total 2 marks]

Score:

9

Circuits — The Basics

1   This question is about electricity supplies.   (Grade 3-4)

   a)   Which describes the UK mains electricity supply?

     ☐ **A** 230 V a.c.   ☐ **B** 320 V a.c.   ☐ **C** 230 V d.c.   ☐ **D** 320 V d.c.

[1]

   b)   Cells and batteries provide a d.c. supply. State what **d.c.** stands for and explain what it means.

....

....

[2]

[Total 3 marks]

2   A student wants to produce a graph of current against voltage for component X.   (Grade 4-6)
An incomplete diagram of the circuit he is going to use is shown below.

component X

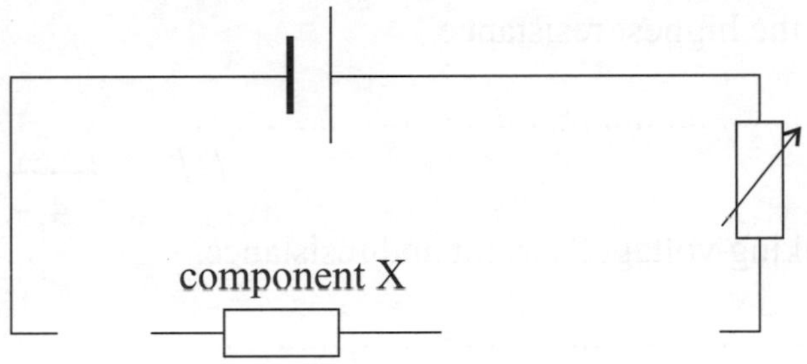

   a)   Complete the circuit by adding an ammeter and a voltmeter.

[2]

   b)   The student increases the resistance of the variable resistor while keeping the voltage of the power supply the same. State what will happen to the current in the circuit.

....

[1]

   c)   Describe a method the student could use to obtain a good set of data to produce his graph from.

....

....

....

....

....

[4]

[Total 7 marks]

Score: ☐

10

Resistance and $V = I \times R$

1 A direct current of 3.0 A flows through a circuit consisting of a battery and a 6.0 Ω resistor. What is the potential difference across the resistor?

Grade 4-6

☐ **A** 0.5 V

☐ **B** 2 V

☐ **C** 9 V

☐ **D** 18 V

[Total 1 mark]

2 The diagram shows current-voltage (*I-V*) graphs for four resistors at a constant temperature.

Grade 6-7

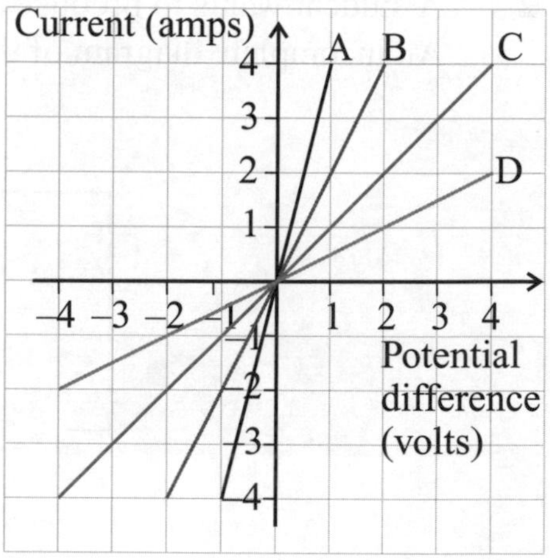

a) State which resistor has the highest resistance.

....
[1]

b) i) State the equation linking voltage, current and resistance.

....
[1]

ii) Calculate the resistance of resistor B.

Resistance = ... Ω
[3]

iii) The resistance of resistor B is tested at different temperatures. At 30 °C, it has a resistance of 0.75 Ω when the voltage across it is 15 V. Calculate the current through the resistor at 30 °C.

Current = ... A
[3]

[Total 8 marks]

3 A student tries to identify two components using a standard test circuit.
The table below shows his readings of current and voltage for the two components.

Voltage (V)	−4.0	−3.0	−2.0	−1.0	0.0	1.0	2.0	3.0	4.0
Component A current (A)	0.0	0.0	0.0	0.0	0.0	0.2	1.0	2.0	4.5
Component B current (A)	−4.0	−3.5	−3.0	−2.0	0.0	2.0	3.0	3.5	4.0

a) State what type of component the data suggests component A is, and justify your choice.

....

....

[2]

b) Plot a current-voltage (*I-V*) graph for component B on the graph paper. Draw a curve of best fit.

[4]

c) i) What type of component is component B?

....

[1]

ii) Explain the changes in the slope of the *I-V* graph for component B between 0 V and 4 V.

....

....

....

[3]

[Total 10 marks]

Exam Practice Tip

There are four types of *I-V* graphs that you need to know — resistors, wires, metal filament lamps and diodes. Make sure you've got their shapes etched on your memory and can describe how current varies with voltage.

Score

☐

___

19

 ☐   ☐   ☐

Section 2 — Electricity

LDRs, Thermistors and LEDs

1 The diagram below shows a circuit that contains an LED, a light-dependent resistor and a cell.

Grade 4-6

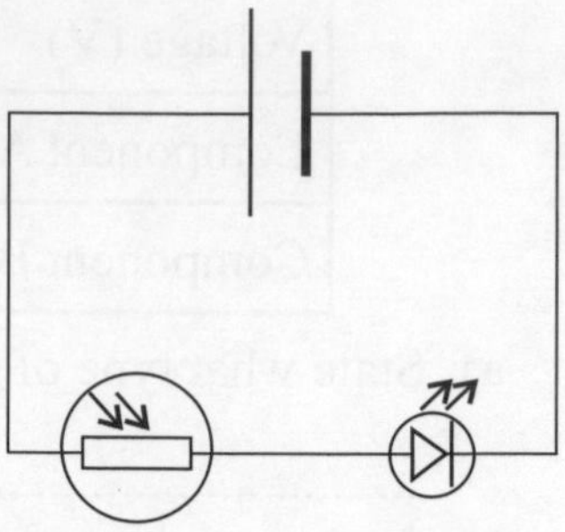

a) Describe how you could tell that a current is flowing in the circuit.

....
[1]

b) The circuit is placed in a well lit room. At the end of the day, the lights in the room are turned off. State and explain how the resistance of the circuit changes when the room lights are switched off.

....

....
[2]

[Total 3 marks]

2 This question is about circuit components.

Grade 6-7

a) i) Which circuit symbol below represents a fuse?

☐ A 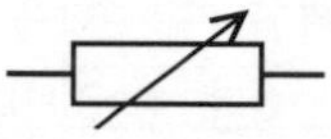   ☐ B 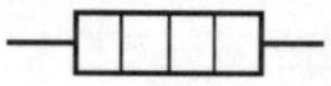   ☐ C 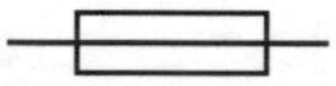   ☐ D 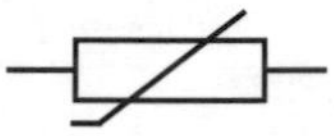
[1]

ii) Which circuit symbol below does **not** represent a type of power source?

☐ A 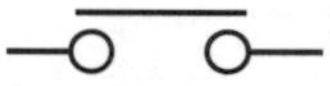   ☐ B    ☐ C 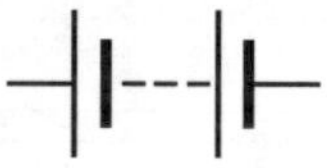   ☐ D
[1]

b) i) Draw a circuit diagram to represent a circuit in which the brightness of a lamp depends on temperature. The circuit should contain **three** components.

[3]

ii) Describe and explain how the current in the circuit changes as the room temperature increases.

....

....
[2]

[Total 7 marks]

Score: ☐

10

Series and Parallel Circuits

1 Two light bulbs are wired in series with a 12 V battery. (Grade 6-7)

a) Give **one** advantage of wiring the lights in parallel instead.

....

[1]

b) The current through one of the bulbs is 0.5 A. Calculate the total resistance in the series circuit.

Resistance = ... Ω

[3]

c) Describe how the current in the circuit would change if there were three bulbs in series connected to the same battery.

....

[1]

[Total 5 marks]

2 The diagram below shows a parallel circuit. (Grade 6-7)

a) The battery supplies a voltage of 4.2 V. Give the voltages V_1 and V_2.

V_1 = ... V

V_2 = ... V

[1]

b) Each resistor has a resistance of 2.0 Ω. Calculate the current through R_2.

Current = ... A

[4]

[Total 5 marks]

Score: ☐

10

Charge, Voltage and Energy Change

1   A 3 V battery can supply a current of 5 A for 20 minutes before it needs recharging.   (Grade 6-7)

a) i)   State what is meant by **current**.

....

[1]

ii) State what carries charge in an electric current through a metal conductor.

....

[1]

b) i)   State the equation that links charge, current and time.

....

[1]

ii) Calculate how much charge will pass through the circuit before the battery needs recharging.

Charge = ... C

[3]

c)   State how much energy is transferred by the battery per coulomb of charge passed
through the circuit. Explain your answer.

....

....

....

[2]

d)   A different battery is used to supply electricity to a circuit. It transfers a charge of 12 C over
3.0 seconds. Calculate the resistance of the circuit if 36 J of energy is transferred in 3.0 s.

Resistance = ... Ω

[4]

[Total 12 marks]

Electrical Safety

1   The figure below shows an old-fashioned household fuse box.

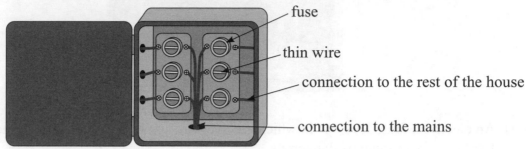

- fuse
- thin wire
- connection to the rest of the house
- connection to the mains

a) Explain why houses have fuse boxes.

    ....
                                                                                        [1]

b) In old-fashioned fuse boxes like this, home-owners sometimes replaced old fuses with pennies.
    Explain why replacing fuses with pennies like this was dangerous.

    ....

    ....
                                                                                        [1]
                                                                                [Total 2 marks]

2   A kitchen appliance manufacturer is checking that their products
    are safe for use in the home. The manufacturer sells a toaster with
    a metal case. It is wired with an earth wire and a fuse for safety.

a) Explain how the earth wire and fuse work when a fault develops in the toaster
    leading to the live wire touching the metal casing.

    ....

    ....

    ....

    ....

    ....
                                                                                        [4]

b) They also make a kettle with a plastic case.
    The kettle is not wired with an earth wire. Explain why the kettle is still safe to use.

    ....

    ....
                                                                                        [2]
                                                                                [Total 6 marks]

3 A microwave oven has a metal casing.

a) i) An electrical fault develops in which the live wire comes into contact with the metal casing.
Explain why this can be dangerous.

....

....

[1]

ii) The microwave oven is connected to a circuit breaker. Describe what happens to make the
microwave oven safe again when the fault in part i) occurs.

....

....

....

....

[3]

b) i) Some circuits are protected by fuses.
Describe the main difference between how a fuse and a circuit breaker work.

....

....

[2]

ii) Give **two** advantages of using circuit breakers instead of fuses to protect a circuit.

1 ....

....

2 ....

....

[2]

[Total 8 marks]

Exam Practice Tip

Fuses and circuit breakers don't just safeguard you in the home — knowing all about them could save your
bacon in the exam too. There aren't any equations, but you do need to know how insulation, fuses, earthing
and circuit breakers work, and how they keep us and our gadgets safe if things go wrong.

Score

16

Energy and Power in Circuits

1 The heating element in a kettle usually contains a coil of wire made of Nichrome. When the kettle is turned on, current flows through the coil of wire.

Grade 6-7

a) Explain why the coil of wire in the heating element is designed to have a high resistance.

....

....

....

[2]

b) The table below shows the power and voltage ratings for two kettles.

	Power (kW)	Voltage (V)
Kettle A	2.8	230
Kettle B	3.0	230

i) State the equation linking electrical power, voltage and current.

....

[1]

ii) Calculate the current drawn from the mains supply by kettle A.

Current = ... A

[3]

iii) What current rating should the fuse in kettle A have?

☐ **A** 1 A   ☐ **B** 3 A   ☐ **C** 5 A   ☐ **D** 13 A

[1]

iv) A student is deciding whether to buy kettle A or kettle B. She wants to buy the kettle that boils water faster. Both kettles are 90% efficient. Suggest which kettle she should choose. Give a reason for your answer.

....

....

[2]

[Total 9 marks]

Exam Practice Tip

It's important that you can comfortably use equations for energy and power to work out what fuse an appliance should be fitted with. The most common fuse ratings in the UK are 3 A, 5 A and 13 A and you should pick one just above the normal operating current to avoid it blowing when there's no danger, or not blowing at all.

Score

☐

9

 ☐   ☐   ☐

Static Electricity

1 This question is about the electrical properties of different materials.

a) State what is meant by an electrical insulator.

....

[1]

b) Complete the table below.

Material	Electrical conductor?	Electrical insulator?
Glass	No	Yes
Water	Yes	No
Plastic	....	....
Copper	....	....

[2]

[Total 3 marks]

2 A man walks up some carpeted stairs. The handrail is made of metal and is electrically connected to earth. When he puts his hand near the rail, there is a spark.

Grade 7-9

a) The carpet and the man's shoes rub together, making the man electrically charged. Explain why there is a spark between the man's hand and the rail.

....

....

....

[2]

b) Given that the spark leapt from the man to the handrail, was the man positively charged or negatively charged? Explain your answer.

....

....

....

....

[3]

[Total 5 marks]

Score:

8

Static Electricity and Friction

1 A student rubs a polythene rod with a dusting cloth. The rod becomes negatively charged and the dusting cloth becomes positively charged.

Grade 6-7   PRACTICAL

a) Describe what happens to the electrons as the polythene rod is rubbed.

....

....
[2]

b) The polythene rod is now suspended from a string tied around its centre. The student has another charged object, with an unknown charge on it. Explain how the student can use the negatively charged polythene rod to determine the type of charge (positive or negative) on the object.

....

....

....

....
[3]

[Total 5 marks]

2 The diagram on the right shows a gold-leaf electroscope.

Grade 7-9   PRACTICAL

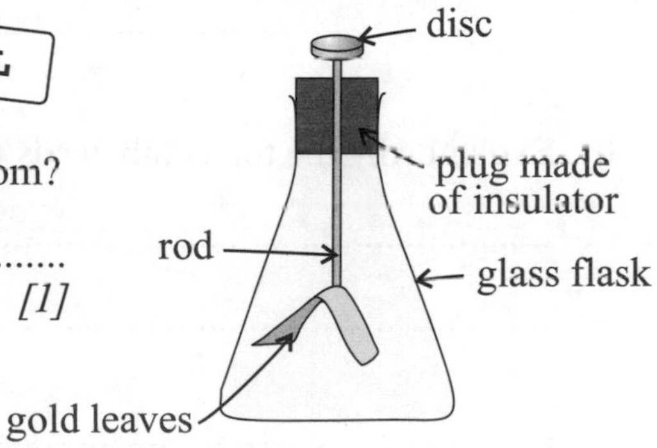

a) What type of material are the disc and rod usually made from?

....
[1]

b) Describe how the gold-leaf electroscope can be used to see whether a material is charged.

disc — plug made of insulator — glass flask — rod — gold leaves

....

....

....

....
[2]

c) State whether or not the electroscope is able to distinguish between positively-charged and negatively-charged objects. Explain your answer.

....

....

....
[3]

[Total 6 marks]

3 A Van de Graaff generator is a machine which is used to generate static electricity. A student uses one type of Van de Graaff generator in class and writes the following description of how it works.

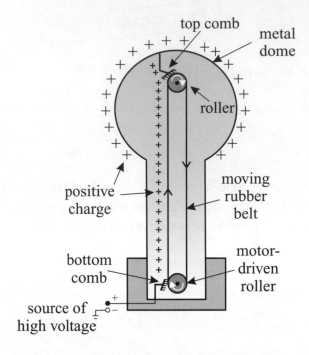

- The bottom comb is positively charged and attracts electrons away from the rubber belt.

- The rubber belt loses electrons and becomes positively charged.

- As the positive charge on the belt passes the top comb, electrons are attracted from the metal dome onto the belt.

- The metal dome loses electrons and builds up a positive static charge.

a) Explain why the belt is made from rubber.

....

....

[2]

b) Explain why the top comb needs to be made from a conductor.

....

....

[1]

c) Explain why electrons are attracted from the metal dome to the belt.

....

....

[1]

d) A student standing on an insulating block places a hand onto the dome of a Van de Graaff generator. Her hair begins to spread apart and stand on end. Explain why this happens.

....

....

....

[3]

[Total 7 marks]

Score: ☐

18

Static Electricity — Examples

1 A tall building is fitted with a lightning rod, made from a conductor, that safely directs charge to earth when the building is struck by lightning. Explain how lightning is caused.

....

....

....

....

....

[Total 2 marks]

Lightning rod

Earth

2 When refuelling a vehicle, fuel flows out of a fuel nozzle and into the vehicle's fuel tank.

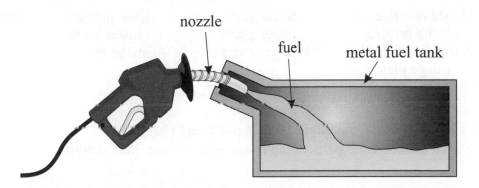

nozzle

fuel

metal fuel tank

a) Explain why it is dangerous if static charge is allowed to build up during this process.

....

....

[2]

b) Give **two** safety measures that can be taken to reduce the build-up of static charge when fuelling.

1 ....

....

2 ....

....

[2]

[Total 4 marks]

3 | A student prints a document from a computer using an inkjet printer. | (Grade 7-9)

a) An inkjet printer works by firing charged droplets of ink towards a piece of paper.
Explain how the printer can control and alter the direction of the droplets of ink.

....

....

....

....

[3]

b) The student then photocopies the document. The diagram below shows the main steps that a photocopier uses to make a paper copy of a document.

Original document → Positively-charged image plate

Light source

Light is reflected off the original document onto the image plate.

Some of the image plate loses its charge.

Negatively-charged black powder

Black powder transferred to image plate.

Paper

Powder transferred to paper.

i) Before the process starts, the image plate is positively charged.
Describe what causes some parts of the image plate to lose their charge.

....

....

[1]

ii) Describe how the original image is transferred to the paper after the light source has been reflected off it.

Think about what's attracted to what throughout the process.

....

....

....

....

....

[5]

[Total 9 marks]

Score:

15

Section 2 — Electricity

Waves — The Basics

1   Waves can be either transverse or longitudinal.   (Grade 3-4)

a) A student uses a spring to produce the two types of waves shown — type A and type B.

type A   type B

State, with reasons, which wave is transverse and which wave is longitudinal.

....

....

....

[2]

b) Give **one** example of a type A wave other than a wave on a spring.

....

[1]

[Total 3 marks]

2   A wave in a pond, travelling at 0.5 m/s, makes a
    floating ball move up and down twice every second.   (Grade 6-7)

wave speed 0.5 m/s

a) What is the frequency of the wave?

Frequency = ... Hz

[1]

b) i) State the equation linking wave speed, frequency and wavelength.

....

[1]

ii) The ball is on a crest of the wave. Calculate how far away the next crest is from the ball.

Distance = ... m

[2]

iii) Calculate the time period of the wave.

Time period = ... s

[2]

[Total 6 marks]

3 The diagram shows the graphs of waves A, B and C. Each graph has the same scale.

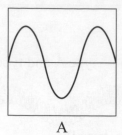 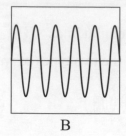 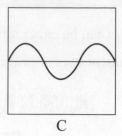

A   B   C

a) What is meant by the **amplitude** of a wave?

....

....

[1]

b) Which of the following is correct?

☐ **A** A and B have the same wavelength.

☐ **B** B and C have the same wavelength.

☐ **C** A and C have the same wavelength.

☐ **D** None of the waves have the same wavelength.

[1]

c) A student uses a ripple tank to produce a water wave. He measures an amplitude of 1 cm and a wavelength of 2 cm and draws a graph of the wave, as shown in the diagram.

height of the wave from
the rest position in cm

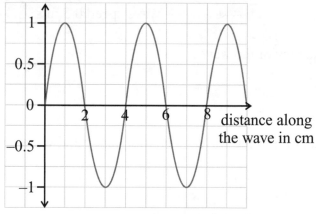

distance along
the wave in cm

i) Which property of the wave has the student drawn **incorrectly**? Explain your answer.

....

[1]

ii) On the same set of axes, sketch a wave with a wavelength of 6 cm and an amplitude of 0.75 cm.

[2]

[Total 5 marks]

Score:

14

Wave Behaviour and EM Waves

1 Some satellite signals are microwaves. **Grade 4-6**

Think about the order of the electromagnetic spectrum.

a) Which of the following is high-frequency microwave radiation closest in frequency to?

☐ **A** high-frequency ultraviolet ☐ **C** low-frequency visible light

☐ **B** high-frequency radio waves ☐ **D** low-frequency infrared

[1]

b) State, with a reason, whether microwave signals travel faster in free space than radio signals.

....

[1]

[Total 2 marks]

2 The Doppler effect can be used to learn information about distant stars. **Grade 6-7**

a) State what is meant by the **Doppler effect**.

....

....

[2]

b) Explain why the Doppler effect occurs.

....

....

....

....

[3]

c) An astronomer finds that the frequencies of the electromagnetic waves emitted by a distant star appear to be slightly lower than those of a similar star that is known not to be moving either towards or away from the Earth.

Suggest whether this indicates that the distant star is moving towards or away from the Earth, and explain your reasoning.

....

....

....

[2]

[Total 7 marks]

Score: ☐

9

 ☐   ☐   ☐

Uses of Electromagnetic Waves

1 The diagram shows electromagnetic radiation being used to sterilise a surgical instrument. *(Grade 3-4)*

a) State what type of electromagnetic radiation is being used.

....
[1]

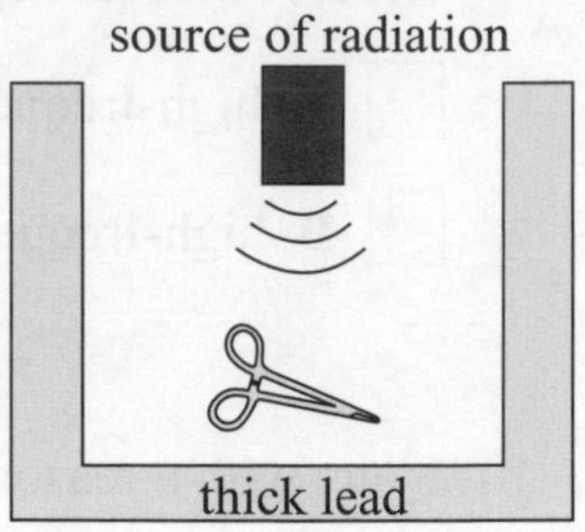

b) A similar process can be used to treat fruit before it is exported to other countries. Suggest why this process is used.

....

....
[2]

source of radiation

thick lead

[Total 3 marks]

2 Microwaves can be used to cook food. *(Grade 4-6)*

Describe how food is heated when cooked in a microwave oven.

....

....

....
[Total 3 marks]

3 Optical fibres have many practical uses. *(Grade 4-6)*

a) Which type of electromagnetic wave is typically transmitted in optical fibres?

☐ **A** radio waves   ☐ **B** visible light   ☐ **C** microwaves   ☐ **D** X-rays
[1]

b) Explain how data is transmitted through optical fibres.

....

....

....
[2]

c) Give **one** application of optical fibres.

....
[1]

[Total 4 marks]

4 A naturalist uses a night vision camera to capture an image of a fox, as shown below.

Explain how the night vision camera allowed this image to be taken.

....

....

....

....

[Total 2 marks]

5 The radio transmitter shown transmits long-wave and short-wave radio signals. The house receiving the signal is a long way from the transmitter.

radio transmitter

a) Describe how the long-wave and short-wave radio signals from the transmitter are each able to reach the house.

Long-wave: ....

....

Short-wave: ....

....

[2]

b) The owner of the house decides to get satellite TV installed.

i) State what type of electromagnetic radiation is used to send signals to satellites.

....

[1]

ii) Describe how satellite TV signals are transmitted from a transmitter on the ground to the house.

....

....

[2]

[Total 5 marks]

6 X-rays are used by truck scanners at country border control points.

Grade 6-7

a) X-rays are passed through a truck. Explain how an image of the objects in the truck is formed.

....

....

....

....

[4]

b) During a scan, the driver and any passengers are asked to step outside the vehicle for their safety. Suggest why this happens.

....

....

[2]

[Total 6 marks]

7 Ultraviolet radiation can damage skin cells and cause cancer in humans.

Grade 7-9

a) Fluorescent lamps make use of ultraviolet radiation.
State whether or not fluorescent lamps are harmful to humans. Explain your answer.

....

....

....

[2]

b) Photographers sometimes use ultraviolet filters to prevent ultraviolet radiation from reaching the camera's sensor or film. Describe how a camera creates a photograph using visible light, and how the camera and the photographer can control the amount of visible light entering it.

....

....

....

....

[3]

[Total 5 marks]

Exam Practice Tip

This stuff isn't too bad — no calculations or tricky equations here. Try writing down the types of electromagnetic wave on some revision cards and scribbling descriptions of their applications on the back. See if you can describe the applications for each type of wave before checking the backs of the cards.

Score

28

Dangers of Electromagnetic Waves

1   Living cells in the human body can absorb gamma rays.   *Grade 4-6*

  a) Give **two** damaging effects that gamma rays can have when they are absorbed by living cells.

   1 ....

   2 ....

   [2]

  b) Gamma radiation can be used to treat cancer. Give **one** precaution that
      should be taken when giving a cancer patient a dose of gamma radiation.

   ....

   [1]

   [Total 3 marks]

2   Sunlight contains ultraviolet radiation.   *Grade 4-6*

  a) Explain why excessive sunbathing can be dangerous.

   ....

   ....

   [2]

  b) Describe **one** method of protecting yourself from the sun.

   ....

   ....

   [1]

   [Total 3 marks]

3   Mobile phones use microwaves to transmit signals.   *Grade 6-7*

  a) Suggest why people might be worried that excessive mobile phone use could be harmful.

   ....

   ....

   [1]

  b) Explain why it would be more dangerous to use infrared radiation instead of microwaves for
      mobile phone signals.

   ....

   ....

   [2]

   [Total 3 marks]

   Score: [   ]

   9

Section 3 — Waves

Reflection and Refraction of Waves

1 A student shines a beam of light into a mirror. **(Grade 6-7)**

   a) i) State the **law of reflection**.

....

....

[1]

    ii) State what is meant by **diffuse reflection**.

....

....

[1]

   b) A ray of light with an angle of incidence of 35° is reflected from a mirror.
Sketch a ray diagram to show this below. The mirror and the normal have been drawn for you.

Normal – – – – – – – – – – – – – – – – –

[2]

   c) The student swaps the mirror for a glass block, and shines the beam of light into
it at an angle to the normal. Explain why the beam of light changes direction
when it travels from the air into the block and state the name of this effect.

....

....

....

[3]

[Total 7 marks]

Exam Practice Tip

Ray diagrams are used a lot when talking about reflection, so you should get comfortable drawing them.
No matter how complicated any diagram seems, it all comes down to a few simple rules. First, make sure
your lines are straight (unless the ray is changing direction at a boundary). Draw arrowheads on the rays
and make sure they point in the direction the ray is travelling in. Most importantly, always use a protractor
to show that reflected rays obey the law of reflection.

Score

7

More About Refraction of Waves

1 The diagram shows a ray of red light entering a glass prism.

Grade 7-9

PRACTICAL

normal

incident ray

glass prism

air

a) Complete the diagram to show the ray passing through the prism and emerging from the other side. Label the angles of incidence, i, and refraction, r, for both boundaries.

[3]

b) Describe an experiment that you could do to measure i and r at both boundaries.

....

....

....

....

....

....

[4]

c) When a ray of white light enters the prism, several rays of light, each of a separate colour, emerge from the prism. Each ray of light travels in a slightly different direction.

i) Explain why this happens.

....

....

....

[2]

ii) When white light shines through a rectangular block of glass instead of through a triangular prism, all the light that emerges travels in the same direction. Explain why.

....

....

....

[2]

[Total 11 marks]

Score:

11

Section 3 — Waves

Refractive Index and Snell's Law

1 A student is investigating the refractive index of a block of transparent material. She shines a ray of yellow light at the block at various angles of incidence (i) and measures the angles of refraction (r). The table shows her results.

i	r	sin i	sin r
10.0°	8.3°	0.174	0.144
20.0°	16.4°	0.342	0.282
30.0°	24.8°	0.500	0.419
40.0°	32.3°	0.643	0.534
50.0°	39.8°	0.766	0.640
60.0°	46.2°	0.866	0.722

a) Use the values in the table to draw a graph of sin r against sin i.
Plot sin r on the vertical axis, and sin i on the horizontal axis.

[4]

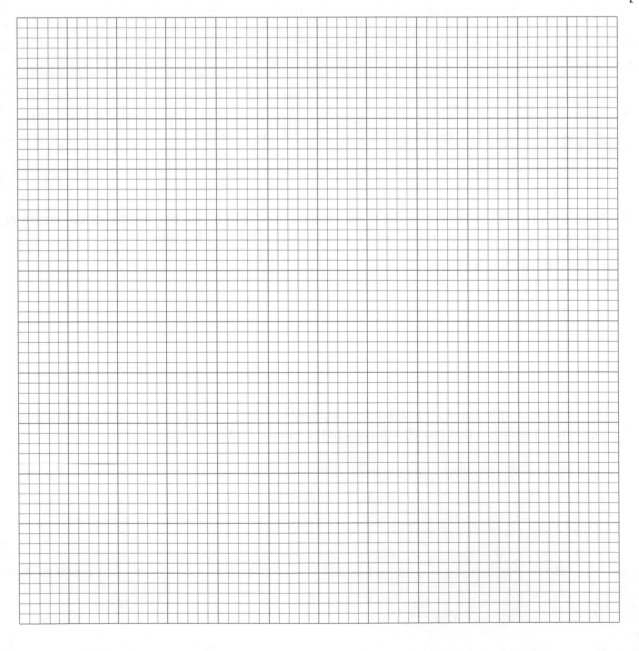

b) The gradient of the graph is equal to $\frac{1}{n}$, where n is the refractive index of the block.

    i) Calculate the gradient of the graph.

gradient = ...

[2]

    ii) Calculate the refractive index of the block.

Refractive index = ...

[2]

[Total 8 marks]

2   The diagram shows white light refracting at an air-glass boundary and separating into colours. **Grade 7-9**

a) The refractive index of glass for red light is 1.514. Calculate the angle of refraction for red light.

Angle of refraction = ...°

[3]

b) Explain why the ray of white light would not separate into colours if it crossed the boundary along the normal.

....

....

[2]

c) The refractive index of glass for violet light is 1.528. Calculate the angle θ shown in the diagram.

θ = ...°

[4]

[Total 9 marks]

Score:

17

Section 3 — Waves

Refractive Index and Critical Angles

1   Endoscopes use optical fibres to look inside a patient's body. When light meets the boundary between the optical fibre core and the outer cladding, there is total internal reflection.

   a) An optical fibre core has a refractive index of 1.54. Calculate the critical angle of the core material.

   Critical angle = ...°

   [3]

   b) Explain why bending the endoscope too sharply may result in reduced image quality.

   Think about how the angle of incidence will change.

   ....

   ....

   ....

   [2]

   [Total 5 marks]

2   A semicircular acrylic block is placed in water. Light passes through the block into the water. The critical angle (C) of the acrylic-water boundary for the light is 63.2°.

   Grade 6-7   **PRACTICAL**

   a) State what is meant by the **critical angle** for a boundary.

   ....

   [1]

   b) A ray of light meets the acrylic-water boundary at an angle of incidence of 75°.
      Describe what will happen to the ray of light at the boundary.

   ....

   [1]

   c) The diagram shows a ray of light hitting the boundary between the same acrylic block and the air.
      Calculate the refractive index of the acrylic.

   41.8°

   acrylic
   air

   Refractive index = ...

   [3]

   [Total 5 marks]

Exam Practice Tip

Don't forget, total internal reflection only happens when light is going from a material with a higher refractive index to a material with a lower refractive index. The cladding of an optical fibre must have a lower refractive index than the core, otherwise light will always escape, no matter how large the angle of incidence.

Score

10

Sound Waves

1 The diagram shows how an oscilloscope can be used to display sound waves by connecting microphones to it. Trace 1 shows the sound waves detected by microphone 1 and trace 2 shows the sound waves detected by microphone 2.

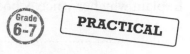

a) i) A student uses the equipment to find the speed of sound. The steps below show a method he can use. Put them into the correct order by numbering the boxes. The first has been done for you.

Statements	Order
Measure the distance between the microphones. This is the wavelength.	
Stop moving microphone 2 when the traces line up.	
Use the measured distance and the frequency of the signal generator to find the wave speed.	
Begin with both microphones at an equal distance from the speaker.	1
Keeping microphone 1 fixed, slowly move microphone 2 away from the speaker (keeping it in line with microphone 1), causing trace 2 to move.	

[3]

ii) With the signal generator set to 50 Hz, the distance between the microphones was measured to be 6.8 m. Calculate the speed of sound in air.

Speed = ... m/s

[2]

b) One microphone is removed and the signal generator is adjusted. The diagram shows the trace produced on the oscilloscope.

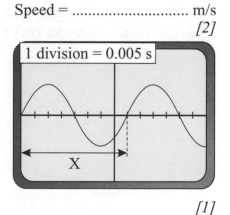

i) Which quantity is represented by quantity X on the trace?

☐ **A** wavelength ☐ **C** frequency

☐ **B** amplitude ☐ **D** time period

[1]

ii) Calculate the frequency of the wave.

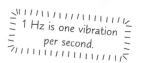
1 Hz is one vibration per second.

Frequency = ... Hz

[2]

iii) On the diagram, draw a waveform for a sound that has the same frequency but is louder.

[1]

[Total 9 marks]

Section 3 — Waves

Paper 2

2 A student sings in her school choir. She practises in both an empty drama hall and on the school playing field. She notices that her voice echoes only when she sings in the drama hall.

Grade 6-7

a) Explain why her voice echoes in the drama hall but not on the playing field.

....

....

[1]

b) Some of the sound produced by the student passes through the walls of the hall. As it does this, its speed increases and its wavelength increases.

Suggest **one** other way the sound may change as it passes through the hall walls.

....

[1]

c) Another student joins in the practice. His voice has a much lower pitch.

i) State the range of frequencies a student with good hearing should be able to hear.

....

[1]

ii) How does the frequency of sound produced by the male student compare to the frequency of sound produced by the female student? Explain your answer.

....

....

[2]

d) The two students are recorded with two different microphones. The microphones are connected to an oscilloscope, which gives the display shown below. Does trace A display the male student's voice or the female student's voice? Justify your answer.

....

....

[1]

[Total 6 marks]

Exam Practice Tip

Describing an experiment to measure the speed of sound could bag you loads of marks. To get top marks, you'll need to be really familiar with all the details, including what you'll measure, what you'll use to measure it, and the formulas you'll need to use. It's tricky stuff, for sure, but you need to get your head round it.

Score

15

Conservation of Energy

1 This question is about energy transfers.

Use options from the box to complete the table below. For each scenario, state the energy store that energy is transferred away from. Each option may be used once.

elastic potential	chemical
gravitational potential	nuclear

Scenario	Energy Transferred From...
A skydiver falling from an aeroplane.	.... energy store
A substance undergoing a nuclear reaction.	.... energy store
A stretched spring returning to its original shape.	.... energy store
A piece of burning coal.	.... energy store

[Total 3 marks]

2 A kettle of cold water is plugged into the mains and brought to the boil. Energy is transferred from the mains to the water.

a) Name the energy store of the water that the energy is transferred **to**.

....

[1]

b) How is energy transferred from the mains to the kettle?

☐ **A** mechanically

☐ **B** by heating

☐ **C** by radiation

☐ **D** electrically

[1]

c) State the principle of conservation of energy.

....

....

[2]

[Total 4 marks]

Exam Practice Tip

Ah, energy transfers. All you need to know is that energy can <u>never</u> be created or destroyed. What goes into a device must come out. Even better if you can work out which energy stores the energy is being transferred to and from. But if you're not sure, it's usually common sense so try not to panic and you'll figure it out.

Score

☐

7

Efficiency

1 Which of the following washing machines is the most efficient?

Washing machine	Input energy (J)	Useful output energy (J)
☐ A	4×10^4	2.52×10^4
☐ B	4×10^4	2.80×10^4
☐ C	4×10^4	2.95×10^4
☐ D	4×10^4	2.98×10^4

[Total 1 mark]

2 An electric fan transfers 7250 J of energy. 2 kJ of this is wasted energy.

a) Suggest **one** way in which energy is wasted by the fan.

....

[1]

b) Calculate the efficiency of the fan. Give your answer to **2** significant figures.

Efficiency = ... %

[4]

[Total 5 marks]

3 An electric kettle has an efficiency of 76%. 2500 J of energy is transferred from the mains to the kettle every second. When the kettle is full, it needs to transfer 418 000 J of energy to the thermal energy store of the water to boil it.

How long does a full kettle need to be switched on for in order to boil the water?

☐ **A** 2.8 minutes

☐ **B** 22 seconds

☐ **C** 167 seconds

☐ **D** 220 seconds

[Total 1 mark]

	Score
Exam Practice Tip No device is 100% efficient as some energy will always be wasted. For example, energy is carried away by sound waves — you can probably hear an electrical appliance in your home if it's turned on, even if it's just a quiet hum. The device may also heat up — you'll probably have noticed this with things like TVs and laptops.	☐ ――― **7**

Energy Transfers

1   An electric heater is connected to the mains.   **Grade 4-6**

Which statement correctly describes the energy transfer between the mains and the heater?

☐   **A**   Energy is transferred electrically to the kinetic energy store of the heater.

☐   **B**   Energy is transferred by heating to the kinetic energy store of the heater.

☐   **C**   Energy is transferred electrically to the thermal energy store of the heater.

☐   **D**   Energy is transferred by radiation to the thermal energy store of the heater.

[Total 1 mark]

2   A weight lifter is holding a set of weights still above his head.   **Grade 4-6**

a)   Describe the energy transfers involved when the weight lifter raises the weights.

....

....

....

[3]

b)   The weight lifter drops the weights. Describe the energy transfer that will take place as they fall towards the floor.

....

....

[2]

[Total 5 marks]

3   Describe the energy transfers for a golf club hitting a ball, starting with the energy stored in the golf club.   **Grade 6-7**

....

....

....

....

....

[Total 4 marks]

Score: ☐

10

Section 4 — Energy Resources and Energy Transfer

Sankey Diagrams

1 The manufacturer of a clock creates a Sankey diagram to show the energy transfers involved when the clock is in operation.

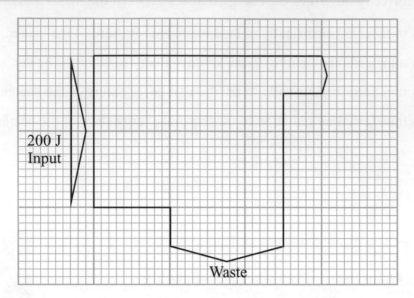

a) Calculate the value represented by each small square on the diagram.

1 square = ... J

[1]

b) Calculate how much energy is transferred usefully by the clock for every 200 J of energy supplied.

Useful energy transferred = ... J

[1]

c) Four fifths of the wasted energy is transferred to thermal energy stores and one fifth is carried away by sound. Use the grid below to draw a Sankey diagram for the clock to show this.

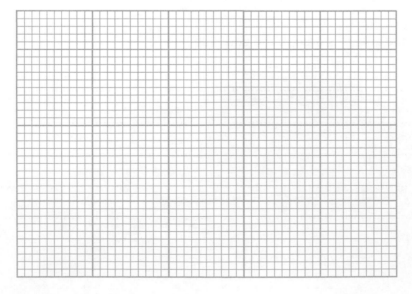

[3]

[Total 5 marks]

2 A crane uses a cable and a hook to lift a weight by winding the cable around a drum. Below is a Sankey diagram for the crane lifting a weight.

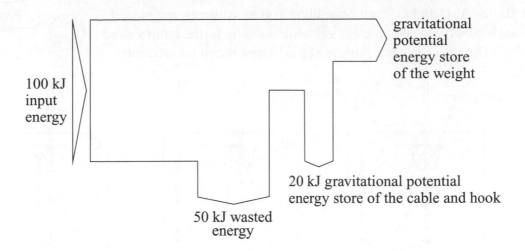

100 kJ input energy

gravitational potential energy store of the weight

20 kJ gravitational potential energy store of the cable and hook

50 kJ wasted energy

a) Suggest **one** energy store that energy is transferred to when energy is wasted by the crane.

....

[1]

b) Calculate the energy transferred to the gravitational potential energy store of the weight by the crane.

Energy = ... kJ

[1]

c) The weight is released and falls to the ground. 1.5 kJ of energy is wastefully transferred to thermal energy stores and carried away by sound, due to air resistance acting on the weight during the fall. Sketch and label a Sankey diagram to show the energy transfers that take place during the weight's fall.

[3]

[Total 5 marks]

Score:

10

Energy Transfer by Heating

1   Three flasks, A, B and C, each containing 100 ml of water, are placed
in closed boxes filled with a clear gel which is at an initial temperature
of 50 °C. The water in each flask is at a different initial temperature.

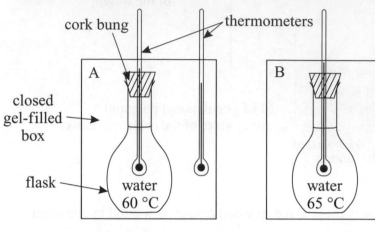

cork bung   thermometers

closed
gel-filled
box

flask

A

water
60 °C

B

water
65 °C

C

water
70 °C

a) Name **two** ways in which the flasks will transfer energy by heating to the gel surrounding them.

1 ....

2 ....

[2]

b) State which flask will transfer energy to the gel the fastest. Explain your answer.

....

....

[2]

[Total 4 marks]

2   A solid block is heated at one end until the temperature of the whole block has increased.

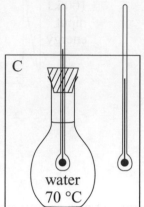

Name the main method of energy transfer by heating in solids. Describe, in terms of particles,
how energy is transferred through the solid block by this method.

....

....

....

....

....

[Total 3 marks]

Score:

7

Section 4 — Energy Resources and Energy Transfer

Convection

1 Energy can be transferred by convection. **(Grade 6-7)** **PRACTICAL**

a) Give the state of matter in which convection cannot take place. Give a reason for your answer.

....

....

[2]

b) A student is carrying out an experiment in class to demonstrate convection.
   She fills a rectangular glass tube with water and heats one of the bottom corners, as shown.

glass tube
filled with
cold water

heater

i) Draw **two** arrows on the diagram above to show the movement of the water within the tube.

[1]

ii) Explain why the water in the pipe moves in the way that you have shown in part i).

....

....

....

....

[3]

c) Which of the following is **not** an example of convection?

☐ **A** the heating of a large room by a radiator

☐ **B** the heating of water in a kettle

☐ **C** the transfer of energy by heating through a copper pan

☐ **D** hot air rising up a chimney

[1]

[Total 7 marks]

Exam Practice Tip

An exam favourite is to show you a situation and get you to explain how convection is involved.
Just remember that whatever kind of substance is involved, the process is pretty much always the same —
the hot stuff rises, the cold stuff sinks and gets heated, and the whole thing repeats.

Score

☐

7

More Energy Transfers by Heating

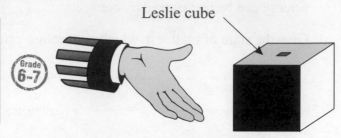

Leslie cube

1 A student uses a Leslie cube, shown in the diagram to the right, to investigate how different surfaces radiate energy. A Leslie cube is a hollow cube with faces that have differently textured and coloured surfaces.

Grade 6-7

The student fills the cube with hot water and places his hand near to each surface.
He records how warm his hand feels in front of each surface.
The four sides of the cube are matt black, shiny black, matt white and shiny white.

a) Predict which side the student's hand would feel warmest in front of.

....

[1]

b) Predict which side the student's hand would feel coolest in front of.

....

[1]

c) Suggest **one** way to improve the student's experiment.

....

[1]

[Total 3 marks]

2 A takeaway coffee cup is designed to reduce the energy transferred away from the hot drink. It is made of paper, and wrapped in corrugated cardboard.

Grade 7-9

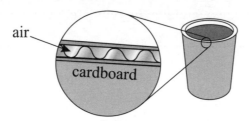

air

cardboard

As shown in the diagram, small pockets of air are trapped by the corrugated cardboard.
Air, paper and cardboard all have low thermal conductivities.
Explain how the design of the cup helps reduce the rate that energy is transferred from the thermal energy store of the hot drink.

....

....

....

....

[Total 3 marks]

Score:

6

Section 4 — Energy Resources and Energy Transfer

Work and Power

1   Which of these is the definition of power?   (Grade 4-6)

☐ **A** Power is the total work done by an object.

☐ **B** Power is the rate of energy transfer.

☐ **C** Power is the total energy transferred to an object.

☐ **D** Power is the minimum work done to an object to cause it to move.

[Total 1 mark]

2   A student is investigating the work done by different washing machines during a standard washing cycle. The table below shows the manufacturer's data about three machines.   (Grade 6-7)

Machine	Power	Time needed
A	600 W	125 minutes
B	400 W	160 minutes
C	....	125 minutes

a) Calculate the work done by machine A during its standard washing cycle.
   Give your answer in kJ.

Work done = ... kJ

[3]

b) Machine C's standard cycle lasts for 125 minutes. It does 3 930 000 J of work in that time.
   Complete the table above by calculating the power of machine C.

[2]

[Total 5 marks]

3 A woman pushes a 20 kg wheelbarrow 15 m along a flat path using a horizontal force of 50 N. **Grade 6-7**

a) i) State the equation that links work done, force applied and distance moved in the direction of the force.

....
[1]

ii) Calculate the work done by the woman.

Work done = ... J
[2]

b) Work has to be done against the frictional forces acting on the wheel of the wheelbarrow. Explain the effect this has on the temperature of the wheel.

....

....

....
[2]

[Total 5 marks]

4 A mechanic replaces a worn out engine of a moped with a new, more powerful one. The new engine is 45% more powerful than the old one. The old engine transferred 1.87×10^3 kJ of energy in 1 hour. **Grade 7-9**

a) Calculate the power of the new engine.

Power = ... W
[4]

b) Explain the effect replacing the engine will have on the time taken for the moped to accelerate from rest to 13 m/s. Assume all the energy transferred by the engines is transferred usefully.

....

....

....

....

....
[3]

[Total 7 marks]

Score: ☐

18

Kinetic and Potential Energy Stores

1 A bird is flying through the sky. (Grade 3-4)

Which of the bird's energy stores contain energy?

☐ **A** gravitational potential energy store only

☐ **B** gravitational potential and kinetic energy stores

☐ **C** kinetic energy store only

☐ **D** neither gravitational potential nor kinetic energy stores

[Total 1 mark]

2 A student climbs up some stairs from the ground floor of a building to a height of 10 m. The student has a mass of 65 kg. (Grade 4-6)

a) State the equation that links the energy stored in the gravitational potential energy store, mass, gravitational field strength (*g*) and height.

....

[1]

b) Calculate the amount of energy in the student's gravitational potential energy store when she reaches the top of the stairs.

$g = 10$ N/kg

Energy = ... J

[2]

[Total 3 marks]

3 A student throws a ball directly upwards. At its highest point, the ball has 4.0 J of energy in its gravitational potential energy store. (Grade 6-7)

a) State how much energy will be in the ball's kinetic energy store just before it hits the ground, assuming no air resistance acts on the ball.

Energy = ... J

[1]

b) State the equation that links the energy in the kinetic energy store, mass and speed.

....

[1]

c) The ball hits the ground with a speed of 8.9 m/s. Calculate the mass of the ball.

Mass = ... kg

[3]

[Total 5 marks]

4 A roller coaster cart with a mass of 105 kg is travelling along a horizontal track at 2.39 m/s.

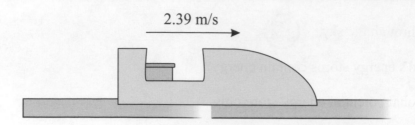

2.39 m/s

a) Calculate the energy in the kinetic energy store of the cart.

Energy = ... J

[2]

b) The cart reaches a downhill slope in the track with a vertical height of 20.2 m.
   It rolls down the slope with no driving force other than gravity.

   i) Calculate the energy lost from the gravitational potential energy store of the cart as it rolls
      down the slope.

*Remember,
g = 10 N/kg.*

Energy = ... J

[2]

   ii) Assuming no frictional forces act against the cart, explain what happens to the energy that is
       lost from the gravitational potential energy store.

   ....

[1]

c) Calculate the speed of the cart at the bottom of the slope, assuming no friction acts
   against the cart.

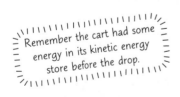

*Remember the cart had some
energy in its kinetic energy
store before the drop.*

Speed = ... m/s

[4]

[Total 9 marks]

Score:

18

Section 4 — Energy Resources and Energy Transfer

Non-Renewable Energy and Power Stations

1 Which of the following energy sources is a renewable energy source?   *Grade 3-4*

☐ **A** coal

☐ **B** nuclear

☐ **C** wind

☐ **D** oil

[Total 1 mark]

2 Which of the following is a possible disadvantage of using non-renewable energy resources to generate electricity?   *Grade 4-6*

☐ **A** They cannot generate electricity at night.

☐ **B** They don't release very much energy.

☐ **C** They can only generate electricity in certain weather conditions.

☐ **D** They can produce sulfur dioxide and cause acid rain.

[Total 1 mark]

3 Natural gas can be used to generate electricity.   *Grade 6-7*

a) Natural gas is a non-renewable energy source. Natural gas is burned in power stations. Describe the energy transfers that occur in a natural gas power station to generate electricity.

....

....

....

....

....

....

[4]

b) Describe **two** advantages of generating electricity using natural gas.

1 ....

....

2 ....

....

[2]

[Total 6 marks]

Score:

8

Section 4 — Energy Resources and Energy Transfer

Nuclear, Wind and Geothermal Power

1 Electricity can be generated using wind and geothermal power. *(Grade 4-6)*

a) i) The diagram below shows the transfers of energy during the generation of electricity using geothermal power. Complete the diagram by adding the types of energy store involved in the energy transfers.

.... → .... → ....

energy store of hot rocks   energy store of water   energy stores of turbine
                                                                          and generator
                                                                                              [3]

ii) Give **one** advantage and **one** disadvantage of generating electricity using geothermal resources.

Advantage = ...

Disadvantage = ...
                                                                                              [2]

b) Give **one** advantage and **one** disadvantage of generating electricity using wind.

Advantage = ...

Disadvantage = ...
                                                                                              [2]
                                                                                    [Total 7 marks]

2 In a nuclear power station, water is heated to produce steam. *(Grade 6-7)*

a) Describe the energy transfer(s) that occur in a nuclear power station to produce the steam.

....

....
                                                                                              [1]

b) i) One argument for building more nuclear power stations is that generating electricity from nuclear fuel does not contribute to global warming. Explain why this is the case.

....
                                                                                              [1]

ii) Give **two** ways in which generating nuclear power can harm the environment.

1 ....

....

2 ....

....
                                                                                              [2]
                                                                                    [Total 4 marks]

Score: ▢

11

Solar and Wave Power

1 In some coastal regions, electricity is generated from waves using wave converters. **Grade 4-6**

a) Which of the following statements about wave converters is true?

☐ **A** They generate electricity all the time.

☐ **B** The initial costs of wave converters are low.

☐ **C** They produce pollution when generating electricity.

☐ **D** They can be hazardous to boats.

[1]

b) Describe the energy transfer that occurs in a wave converter when it is used to generate electricity.

....

....

[1]

[Total 2 marks]

2 Energy from the Sun is used in different ways. **Grade 6-7**

a) Name **one** device that uses energy from the Sun to directly generate electricity.

....

[1]

b) Electricity generated from the Sun's energy can be used to heat water in a home.
Name and describe **one** other way the Sun's energy can be used to heat water in a home.

....

....

[2]

c) Give **two** reasons why electricity generated from the Sun is rarely supplied to the national grid.

1 ....

....

2 ....

....

[2]

[Total 5 marks]

Exam Practice Tip

There are some very common types of questions that examiners like to ask on energy resources. Make sure you can describe the energy transfers involved in using each different type of energy resource to generate electricity, and that you know the advantages and disadvantages of using each resource.

Score

☐

7

 ☐   ☐   ☐   **Section 4 — Energy Resources and Energy Transfer**

Generating Electricity Using Water

1 Water can be used in many ways to generate electricity. In some countries, electricity is generated using hydroelectric dams. Water is held back behind the dam before being allowed to flow out through turbines to produce electricity.

a) Describe the energy transfers involved when water flowing through the turbines is used to produce electricity.

....

....

[2]

b) Hydroelectric power stations don't produce any carbon dioxide when generating electricity. Give **two** ways that using hydroelectric power stations to generate electricity damages the environment.

1 ....

....

2 ....

....

[2]

c) In some hydroelectric power stations, energy is used to pump water back into the reservoir during times of low electricity demand. Give the name of this type of system.

....

[1]

d) Sea tides can also be used to generate electricity using tidal barrages. Give **two** advantages of generating electricity using tidal barrages.

1 ....

....

2 ....

....

[2]

[Total 7 marks]

Score:

7

Paper 2

Density and Pressure

1 A child has a collection of metal toy soldiers of different sizes made from the same metal. **(Grade 3-4)**
Which of the following statements is true?

  ☐ **A** The masses and densities of each of the toy soldiers are the same.

  ☐ **B** The masses of each of the toy soldiers are the same, but their densities may vary.

  ☐ **C** The densities of each of the toy soldiers are the same, but their masses may vary.

  ☐ **D** The densities and masses of each toy soldier may vary.

[Total 1 mark]

2 A student wants to measure the density of a pendant. **(Grade 4-6)** **PRACTICAL**
He can use the equipment shown.

eureka can   measuring cylinder   mass balance

a) State the **two** quantities the student should measure.

1 ....

2 ....

[2]

b) Describe the steps the student could take to find the density of the pendant
with the equipment shown.

....

....

....

....

....

....

[5]

[Total 7 marks]

3 Pressure is a measure of the force applied to the surface of a substance. *(Grade 4-6)*

a) State how the pressure of liquids at rest changes with depth.

....

[1]

b) i) State the equation linking pressure, force and area.

....

[1]

ii) Calculate the pressure created by a force of 18 N acting over an area of 4500 cm².

Pressure = ... Pa

[3]

[Total 5 marks]

4 A company that manufactures a water-resistant digital watch tests the watch under high pressure in salt water. They only recommend it is used underwater if the pressure difference from the surface is 245 kPa or less. *(Grade 6-7)*

a) State the equation linking pressure difference, height, density and the gravitational field strength (*g*).

....

[1]

b) i) The mass of a 0.500 m³ volume of salt water is 514 kg. Calculate the density of salt water.

Density = ... kg/m³

[2]

ii) Calculate the maximum depth from the surface of the salt water that the watch can be used at.

> Remember that the pressure is in kPa. You'll need to convert it to do this calculation.

Maximum depth = ... m

[3]

[Total 6 marks]

Exam Practice Tip

It's important to remember with questions like the last one that it's the **difference** in depth that matters. If you descend to a depth of 4000 m and want to know the pressure difference from when you started, the first thing to ask is "what was my initial depth?" Don't just plug 4000 into the equation if you didn't start at 0.

Score

[ ]
―――
19

Changes of State

1   Substances can exist in different states of matter. (Grade 6-7)

a) i) Describe the arrangement and movement of the particles in a solid.

....

....

[2]

ii) Give the name of the state of matter that possesses the **highest** average energy per particle.

....

[1]

b) If a substance is heated to a certain temperature it can change from a solid to a liquid.

i) Give the name of this process.

....

[1]

ii) Explain why the temperature of the substance does not increase during this process.

....

....

....

[2]

c) If a liquid is heated to a certain temperature it starts to boil and become a gas.

i) Name the other process that causes a liquid to start to become a gas. Explain how it is different to boiling.

....

....

....

....

[3]

ii) Explain why the remaining liquid cools down when a liquid starts to turn into a gas by the process named in part i).

....

....

....

[3]

[Total 12 marks]

Score:

12

Section 5 — Solids, Liquids and Gases

Temperature and Particle Theory

1 The Kelvin scale and the Celsius scale can be used to measure temperature. **Grade 4-6**

a) i) A gas is cooled. Describe what effect this has on the average speed of its particles.

....
[1]

ii) Explain why there is a minimum possible temperature that any substance can reach, known as the absolute zero of temperature.

....

....
[2]

iii) Give the numerical value of the absolute zero of temperature in degrees Celsius.

Temperature = ... °C
[1]

b) Temperature can be converted between the Kelvin and Celsius scales. Complete the table below.

Temperature (K)	Temperature (°C)
10	....
....	631

[2]

[Total 6 marks]

2 The graph on the right shows the temperature of a substance against time as it is heated. **Grade 4-6**

a) Describe what is happening during the period 3-8 minutes from the beginning of heating.

....

....
[1]

b) Give the melting and boiling points of the substance.

Melting point = ... °C   Boiling point = ... °C

[2]

[Total 3 marks]

Score:

9

Section 5 — Solids, Liquids and Gases

Particle Theory and Pressure in Gases

1   A sealed container with a fixed volume is fitted with internal temperature and pressure gauges. The gauges show that the temperature is 288 K and the pressure is 107 kPa inside the container.

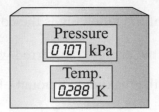

The container is heated so that the temperature of the gas inside it becomes 405 K. Calculate the pressure that will be shown on the pressure gauge.

Pressure = ... kPa

[Total 3 marks]

2   A cylinder sealed with a piston contains 0.014 m³ of gas at a pressure of 98 kPa.

a) i) The piston is squeezed in and the volume containing the gas decreases. State the effect on the gas pressure inside the cylinder. Explain your answer in terms of particle theory.

....

....

....

[3]

ii) The gas is compressed to a volume of 0.013 m³. The temperature of the gas remains constant. Calculate the pressure inside the cylinder after the compression.

Pressure = ... kPa

[3]

b) The cylinder is heated while the piston remains in place to keep its volume constant. State and explain what happens to the pressure inside the cylinder.

....

....

....

[3]

[Total 9 marks]

Score:

12

Specific Heat Capacity

1 Which of the following is the correct definition of specific heat capacity? *(Grade 3-4)*

☐ **A** the energy transferred when an object is burnt

☐ **B** the maximum amount of energy an object can store before it melts

☐ **C** the energy needed to change the temperature of an object by 10 °C per kg of mass

☐ **D** the energy needed to change the temperature of an object by 1 °C per kg of mass

[Total 1 mark]

2 A student uses the equipment listed below to investigate the specific heat capacity of different liquids. *(Grade 7-9)* **PRACTICAL**

- Insulated flask
- Mass balance
- Joulemeter
- Thermometer
- Power supply
- Immersion heater

a) Describe how the student could use the apparatus listed above to calculate the specific heat capacities of different liquids.

....

....

....

....

....

....

....

....

[5]

b) 15 kJ of energy was supplied to each sample. The student then recorded her results, shown in the table below. Complete the table to show the specific heat capacity of liquid C.

Liquid	Mass (kg)	Temperature change (°C)	Specific heat capacity (J/kg °C)
A	0.30	12	4200
B	0.30	23	2200
C	0.30	25	....

[3]

[Total 8 marks]

Exam Practice Tip

Remember, you can also do the above experiment using a voltmeter and an ammeter instead of a joulemeter. Just time how long the heater is on for (in s), and find the energy it has supplied to the liquid using $E = IVt$.

Score

☐

9

Section 5 — Solids, Liquids and Gases

Magnets and Magnetic Fields

1 A student arranges two magnets as shown below. Grade 4-6

N   S   N   S

a) Describe the magnetic field in the shaded region between the dotted lines.

....

[1]

b) State whether there will be a force of attraction, repulsion, or no force between the two magnets. Explain your answer.

....

....

[2]

[Total 3 marks]

2 A student draws the magnetic field lines between four bar magnets, as shown in the diagram. Grade 6-7 **PRACTICAL**

a) Describe an experiment that the student could have done to show this magnetic field pattern.

....

....

....

....

[2]

magnetic field lines   magnets

b) Add **four** arrows to the magnetic field lines on the diagram, one between each set of neighbouring magnets, to show the direction of the magnetic field.

[2]

The student then decides to investigate magnetic materials.

c) Describe what is meant by a **magnetic material**.

....

[1]

d) The head of an iron nail is placed close to the north pole of a bar magnet. The head of the nail is attracted towards the bar magnet until they touch and it sticks to the magnet. Explain why this happens.

....

....

[2]

[Total 7 marks]

Score: ☐

10

 ☐   ☐   ☐

Electromagnetism

1 A student is investigating magnetic fields. She passes a copper rod through a piece of flat card and connects it in an electrical circuit, as shown in the diagram.

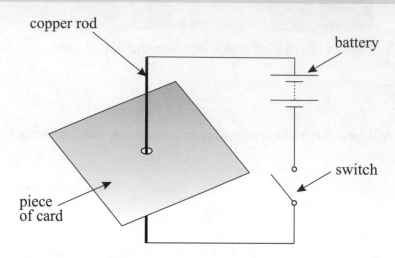

copper rod

battery

switch

piece of card

a) Which of the following correctly describes what happens when the switch is closed?

    ☐ **A** A magnetic field is created around the copper rod.

    ☐ **B** A magnetic field is created by the piece of card.

    ☐ **C** The piece of card becomes magnetic.

    ☐ **D** No magnetic field is created.

[1]

b) Some iron filings are sprinkled onto the card. When the switch is closed, a pattern develops in the iron filings. On the diagram above, sketch the pattern.

[1]

c) The student removes the rod and card and attaches a loop of wire passed through a piece of card to the electrical circuit. The switch is then closed. On the piece of card in the diagram below, sketch the magnetic field produced.

[2]

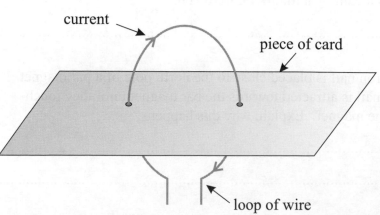

current

piece of card

loop of wire

[Total 4 marks]

Section 6 — Magnetism and Electromagnetism

2 An electromagnet is used by a crane to lift, move and drop iron and steel. **Grade 6-7**

a) The electromagnet contains a solenoid. State what is meant by a **solenoid**.

....

[1]

b) Describe the shape of the magnetic field that a solenoid produces.
You may use a sketch to help with your answer.

....

....

....

[2]

c) When a current is passed through the electromagnet, an iron bar on the ground nearby is attracted to it. When the current is stopped, the bar drops back to the ground. Explain why this happens.

....

....

....

....

[4]

d) The crane's electromagnet contains a magnetically soft iron core.

i) Describe what is meant by a **magnetically soft** material.

....

....

[1]

ii) Explain why putting a magnetically hard core in the electromagnet would cause the crane to not work properly.

....

....

[2]

[Total 10 marks]

Exam Practice Tip

A current-carrying wire will always produce a magnetic field around it. No matter what position the wire is in, or what shape it's been bent into, the magnetic field around it will always depend on the direction of the current. Make sure you're familiar with the magnetic field line patterns of these fields.

Score

[ ]

14

Section 6 — Magnetism and Electromagnetism

The Motor Effect

1 The diagram shows a wire placed between two magnets. *(Grade 6-7)*

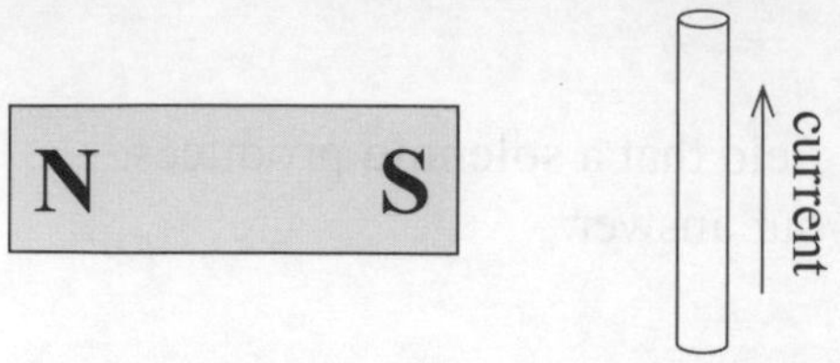

N   S   ↑ current   N   S

a) When a current is passed through the wire, the wire moves.

i) Explain why this happens.

....

....

[1]

ii) State the direction in which the wire will move.

Use Fleming's left-hand rule.

....

[1]

b) i) State what effect increasing the current will have on the force on the wire.

....

[1]

ii) Give **two** ways in which the direction that the force acts could be reversed in this experiment.

1 ....

2 ....

[2]

[Total 5 marks]

---

2 The diagram below shows a free-rolling conducting bar on a set of fixed conducting bars in a magnetic field. All of the conducting bars have a current flowing through them. *(Grade 6-7)*

Explain, in terms of electron movement, why the free-rolling conducting bar doesn't move.

....

....

....

....

....

[Total 2 marks]

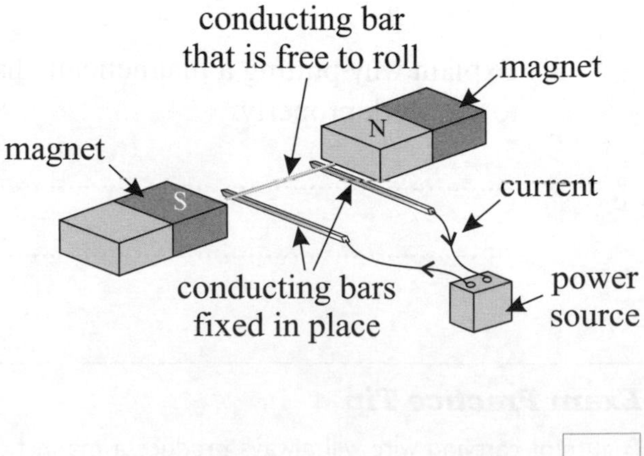

conducting bar
that is free to roll   magnet

magnet   N

S   current

conducting bars   power
fixed in place   source

Score:

7

Electric Motors and Loudspeakers

1 A student is building a simple d.c. motor. He starts by putting a loop of current-carrying wire in a magnetic field, as shown in the diagram. The loop is free to rotate about an axis.

Grade 6-7

direction of rotation   axis of rotation

N   S

B   C

A   D

a) Draw an arrow on the diagram to show the direction of the current in the wire.

Use Fleming's left-hand rule.

[1]

b) The starting position of the loop is shown in the diagram. Explain why the motor will stop rotating in the same direction after a rotation of 90° from its starting position.

....

....

[1]

c) Explain how the student could get the motor to keep rotating in the same direction.

....

....

[2]

d) Give **one** way the motor could be made to rotate faster.

....

[1]

[Total 5 marks]

2 The diagram shows the parts inside an earphone. Sound waves are caused by mechanical vibrations. Explain how the earphone uses an a.c. supply to produce sound waves.

Grade 7-9

coil of wire

cone

permanent magnet

base of the cone

to a.c. supply

....

....

....

....

....

....

....

....

[Total 4 marks]

Score:

9

Section 6 — Magnetism and Electromagnetism

Electromagnetic Induction

1 Which of these is **not** an example of electromagnetic induction? **Grade 3-4**

- [ ] **A** A coil turned in a magnetic field generates a current in the coil.
- [ ] **B** A magnet moved in and out of a solenoid creates a voltage in the solenoid.
- [ ] **C** A current-carrying wire placed between two magnets experiences a force.
- [ ] **D** A rotating bicycle wheel generates electricity by turning a magnet in a coil.

[Total 1 mark]

2 A student uses the rotation of a hamster wheel to power a lamp. **Grade 6-7**

a) Explain why rotating the wheel creates a voltage across the lamp.

....

....

....

[2]

b) Give **two** ways the voltage created across the lamp could be increased.

1 ....

....

2 ....

....

[2]

c) A hamster is put in the wheel to light the lamp. State whether it matters which direction the hamster runs in. Explain your answer.

....

....

[1]

[Total 5 marks]

Section 6 — Magnetism and Electromagnetism

3 The diagram shows a wind-up generator that uses electromagnetic induction to generate an alternating current. The generator is connected to an oscilloscope. The slip rings make sure that each end of the coil remains connected to the same oscilloscope wire.

Grade 7-9

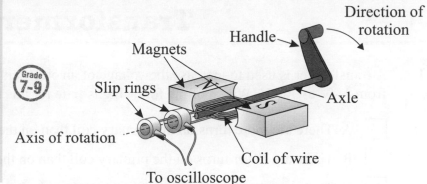

When the handle is rotated in the direction shown in the diagram at a constant speed, the oscilloscope shows the trace below.

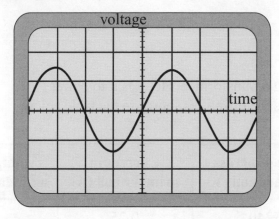

a) Describe how rotating the handle of the generator causes an alternating current to be produced in the circuit connected to the oscilloscope.

....

....

....

[2]

b) Sketch on the diagram a trace that you would see if the handle was rotated faster.

[2]

The position of the coil is then fixed. The magnets are rotated around the axis of rotation as shown in the diagram on the right. The magnets are rotated at the same speed as the coil originally was.

Direction of rotation

Axis of rotation

c) Compare the trace that you would expect to see for this scenario with the trace produced when the coil was rotating at this speed.

....

[1]

[Total 5 marks]

Exam Practice Tip

Electromagnetic induction is basically the opposite of the motor effect — movement causes a voltage and (sometimes) a current. A.c. generators are used to produce loads of the electricity we use, so you might see them applied to all sorts of contexts. Just look out for a changing magnetic field or a moving magnet or wire.

Score

11

Transformers

1 A transformer is used to increase the voltage of an electricity supply from 15 V to 300 V. Which of the following is **true** for this transformer?

Grade 4-6

☐ **A** There are more turns on the primary coil than on the secondary coil.

☐ **B** There are fewer turns on the primary coil than on the secondary coil.

☐ **C** There are the same number of turns on the primary and secondary coils.

☐ **D** There is no secondary coil.

[Total 1 mark]

2 A student is investigating a transformer. He uses it to power a spotlight, and measures the quantities shown in the table below.

Grade 6-7

Voltage across primary coil (V)	Current in primary coil (A)	Voltage across secondary coil (V)
240	0.25	12

a) State, with a reason, whether the transformer is a step-up or step-down transformer.

....

....

[1]

b) i) State the equation linking power, current and voltage.

....

[1]

ii) Calculate the current in the secondary coil when using the spotlight.
   Assume the transformer is 100% efficient.

Current = ... A

[4]

[Total 6 marks]

Paper 2

3 The diagram shows a step-up transformer used to transmit electricity. The secondary coil has 16 times more turns on it than the primary coil.

Grade 7-9

iron core

secondary coil

primary coil

a) Explain how transformers are used to transmit electricity from power stations efficiently and supply the electricity to the consumer safely.

....

....

....

....

....

[3]

b) i) State the equation linking the number of turns on the primary and secondary coils of a transformer and the voltages across the primary and secondary coils.

....

[1]

ii) The voltage across the primary coil is 25 000 V.
Calculate the voltage across the secondary coil.

Voltage = ... V

[3]

c) Explain why a transformer wouldn't work if a direct current was supplied to the primary coil.

....

....

....

[3]

[Total 10 marks]

Score: ☐

17

Section 6 — Magnetism and Electromagnetism

Paper 2

Radioactivity

1   Iodine-131 ($^{131}_{53}$I) is an unstable isotope of iodine.

a) i) Complete the table for an atom of iodine-131.

Particle	Charge	Number present in an atom of iodine-131
Proton	positive	
Neutron	zero	
Electron		53

[3]

ii) Name the particle(s) found in the nucleus of an atom.

....

[1]

b) What is meant by the term **isotopes**?

☐   **A**   atoms with the same atomic number but a different mass number

☐   **B**   atoms with the same mass number but a different atomic number

☐   **C**   atoms with the same proton number but a different atomic number

☐   **D**   atoms with the same number of neutrons but a different number of electrons

[1]

c) Iodine-131 is a waste product of some nuclear power plants and it contributes to the low level of radiation that is present all around us all the time.

i) Give the name of this low level of radiation.

....

[1]

ii) Give **two** natural sources of this low level of radiation.

1 ....

2 ....

[2]

d) Name **four** types of radiation that can be given out when unstable nuclei decay.

....

[4]

[Total 12 marks]

Exam Practice Tip

Make sure you can remember what the mass number and atomic number mean, and how to read the standard atomic notation. You should also remember that neutral atoms have equal numbers of protons and electrons. Get this stuff sorted now, or you'll get stuck later on down the line.

Score

☐

____

12

Ionising Radiation

1 Alpha, beta and gamma radiation can all cause ionisation. **Grade 4-6**

   a) i) Describe what happens to an atom when it is ionised by radiation.

       ....

                                                                           [1]

     ii) State which of alpha, beta and gamma radiation is the most strongly ionising. Explain your answer.

       ....

       ....

                                                                           [2]

   b) i) Name the type of nuclear radiation that is a type of electromagnetic radiation.

       ....

                                                                          [1]

     ii) Name the type of nuclear radiation whose particles are electrons.

       ....

                                                                         [1]

[Total 5 marks]

2 The unstable isotope lead-212 ($^{212}_{82}$Pb) decays by emitting nuclear radiation. After the three stages of decay described below, it becomes a different isotope of lead. **Grade 7-9**

    1. Lead-212 decays by beta decay to become an isotope of bismuth.

    2. The bismuth isotope decays by alpha and gamma decay to become a isotope of thallium.

    3. The thallium isotope decays by beta decay into a different isotope of lead.

  a) Describe what happens to the atomic number and the mass number of a nucleus when it undergoes gamma decay.

     ....

     ....

                                                                             [2]

  b) State the mass number of the lead isotope that is reached in stage 3. Explain your answer.

     ....

     ....

     ....

                                                                             [3]

[Total 5 marks]

Score: ☐

10

 ☐   ☐   ☐

Investigating Radiation and Nuclear Equations

1 A student is doing an investigation to identify the radiation produced by three unknown radioactive sources. The sources were used to pass radiation through thin sheets of paper and aluminium. A detector was used to measure if radiation had passed through the sheets. The results are shown below.

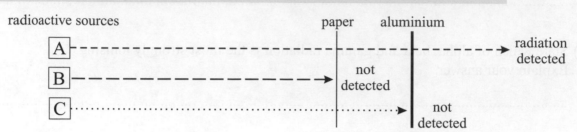

a) Suggest the type of radiation that source C produces. Explain your answer.

....

....

[2]

b) The student uses a Geiger-Müller counter to detect the radiation.
Name **one** other detector that can be used to detect radiation.

....

[1]

c) Explain why the student subtracts the background radiation count from all the readings shown on the detector before she analyses her results.

....

....

[2]

[Total 5 marks]

2 Nuclear equations show what is produced when unstable nuclei decay.

a) Complete the symbol for neutron radiation:

....
n   *[1]*
....

b) Complete this nuclear equation, which shows a polonium isotope decaying by alpha and gamma emission.

$$\text{Po} \longrightarrow {}^{195}_{82}\text{Pb} + \alpha + \gamma$$

An alpha particle can be written as He or α.

[4]

[Total 5 marks]

Score:

10

Section 7 — Radioactivity and Particles

Half-Life

1 Different radioactive samples decay at different rates, known as their activity. *(Grade 3-4)*

a) What are the units of activity?

....

[1]

b) State what is meant by the **half-life** of a radioactive sample.

....

....

[1]

[Total 2 marks]

2 A sample of a radioactive isotope has a half-life of 40 seconds. *(Grade 6-7)*

a) i) The initial activity of the sample is 8000 Bq. Calculate the activity after 2 minutes.

Activity = ... Bq

[2]

ii) Calculate the number of whole minutes it would take for the activity to fall below 200 Bq from its initial activity.

Time = ... mins

[3]

b) Which of the following statements about half life are true?

1. Two samples of the same size but of different isotopes would have the same half-life.

2. Two samples of the same size but of different isotopes would have different half-lives.

3. Two samples of the same isotope of different sizes would have the same half-life.

4. Two samples of the same isotope of different sizes would have different half-lives.

☐ **A** 2 and 3 only

☐ **B** 4 only

☐ **C** 2 and 4 only

☐ **D** None of the statements

[1]

[Total 6 marks]

Section 7 — Radioactivity and Particles

3 A student measured how the activity of a radioactive sample changed with time and used her data to calculate its half-life. Before getting the sample out of storage she measured the activity in the laboratory. When processing the data she subtracted this value from all her activity readings.

a) Suggest why the student recorded the activity in the laboratory before starting the experiment.

....

....
[2]

b) The table below shows the student's processed data. Use the grid to plot a graph of the data. Draw a curved line of best fit.

Time (mins)	Adjusted activity (Bq)
0	740
10	610
20	490
30	400
40	330
60	210
80	140

Use a sharp pencil to draw a neat graph.

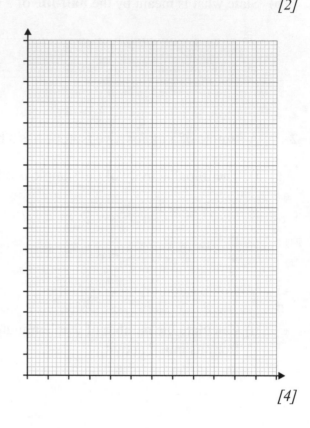

[4]

c) Use your graph to find the half-life of the sample.

Half-life = ... minutes
[1]

d) All of the radioactive samples that the laboratory uses are identical when new. The student decides to repeat the experiment with a sample that is much older than the first. Explain what effect this might have on the data collected.

....

....

....
[2]

[Total 9 marks]

Exam Practice Tip

There's quite a lot of maths involved in half-life questions. Try not to panic though. Just take your time and go through the different stages slowly. Make sure you show your workings too — you might still be able to pick up marks even if you get the final answer wrong. Bonus.

Score

[ ]
___
17

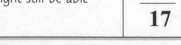

Uses of Nuclear Radiation

1 Nuclear radiation has many uses. (Grade 4-6)

Which of the following sentences is correct?

☐ **A** Alpha radiation can be used to sterilise equipment inside thin metal packaging.

☐ **B** Alpha radiation can be used to gauge the thickness of paper.

☐ **C** Beta radiation can be used to sterilise equipment inside thin metal packaging.

☐ **D** Beta radiation can be used to gauge the thickness of paper.

[Total 1 mark]

2 The unstable isotope iodine-123 is a gamma emitter that is often used as a medical tracer. (Grade 6-7)

a) A healthy thyroid gland absorbs stable iodine and iodine-123 in the same way. Describe how iodine-123 could be used to detect whether the thyroid gland is absorbing iodine as expected.

....

....

....

[2]

b) Explain why alpha emitters cannot be used as tracers in medicine.

....

....

....

....

[4]

c) The table shows the properties of three other radioactive sources.

Source	Half-life	Type of emission
technetium-99m	6 hours	gamma
phosphorus-32	14 days	beta
cobalt-60	5 years	beta/gamma

State which of these would be best to use as a medical tracer. Explain your answer.

....

....

[2]

[Total 8 marks]

Section 7 — Radioactivity and Particles

3 An engineering company knows that one of its pipes is leaking somewhere between two points underground at their site. They are going to use a radioactive source with a short half-life as a tracer to identify the area where the pipe is leaking.

Grade 6-7

a) i) Should the radioactive source they use emit alpha, beta or gamma radiation?

....

[1]

ii) Explain your answer to part i).

....

....

[2]

b) Describe how the company could use the radioactive source to identify the area where the leak is occurring.

....

....

....

[3]

[Total 6 marks]

4 All living things have a fixed ratio of radioactive carbon-14 to stable carbon of $1 : 1 \times 10^{12}$. When they die, the ratio starts to change as the carbon-14 decays and is not replaced.

An ancient wooden artefact was found to have 1 part carbon-14 to 8×10^{12} parts carbon. Carbon-14 has a half-life of 5730 years.
Calculate the amount of time that has passed since the wood was living material.

Grade 7-9

Time = ... years

[Total 3 marks]

Score: [ ]

18

Risks from Nuclear Radiation

1 Radioactive waste emits ionising radiation and has to be carefully disposed of. **Grade 4-6**

a) Explain why exposure to ionising radiation can be dangerous.

....

....

[2]

b) Geological disposal is one method of storing radioactive waste from nuclear power stations. It involves burying the waste hundreds of metres underground, in sealed layers of glass and metal. State and explain **one** reason why this method is used to deal with some forms of radioactive waste.

....

....

[2]

[Total 4 marks]

2 A scientist is concerned about contamination and irradiation in her lab. **Grade 6-7**

a) State what is meant by **contamination**.

....

[1]

b) The scientist is using a low activity radioactive sample. Give **one** example of how she can protect herself from irradiation and **one** example of how she can protect herself from contamination.

Irradiation: ....

Contamination: ....

[2]

[Total 3 marks]

3 Radium-226 is an alpha source that was used in clocks until the 1960s to make the hands and numbers glow. Explain whether a clockmaker should be more concerned about irradiation or contamination when repairing old clocks that contain radium. **Grade 7-9**

....

....

....

....

....

[Total 4 marks]

Score:

11

Nuclear Fission

1   Nuclear fission takes place in nuclear reactors. The diagram
     shows the basic structure of a gas-cooled nuclear reactor.

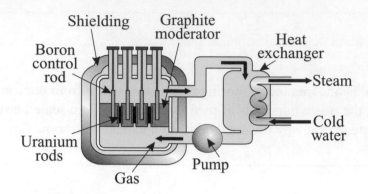

a) Give **one** fuel that can be used in a nuclear reactor.

     ....
                                                                                                                                              [1]

b) i) Describe what happens during a single nuclear fission event, including the products formed.

         ....

         ....

         ....

         ....
                                                                                                                                              [4]

    ii) Explain how nuclear fission can be used to produce energy continuously in a nuclear reactor,
        and how part of the nuclear reactor is designed to help this happen.

         ....

         ....

         ....

         ....
                                                                                                                                              [3]

c) Explain the purpose of the control rods in a nuclear reactor.

     ....

     ....
                                                                                                                                              [1]
                                                                                                                                   [Total 9 marks]

                                                                                                               Score:

                                                                                                                     9

Section 7 — Radioactivity and Particles

Nuclear Fusion

1 Nuclear fusion is a type of nuclear reaction. **Grade 4-6**

Which of the following is an example of a fusion reaction?

☐ **A** $^4_2He \longrightarrow ^2_1H + ^2_1H$

☐ **B** $^1_1H + ^3_1H \longrightarrow ^4_2He$

☐ **C** $^1_0n + ^{235}_{92}U \longrightarrow ^{144}_{54}Xe + ^{90}_{38}Sr + ^1_0n + ^1_0n$

☐ **D** $^{137}_{56}Ba \longrightarrow ^{137}_{56}Ba + ^0_0\gamma$

[Total 1 mark]

2 Energy can be released from nuclear fusion. **Grade 6-7**

a) State what is meant by nuclear fusion.

....
[1]

b) Which of the following statements about nuclear fusion is correct?

☐ **A** total mass of nuclei before nuclear fusion = total mass of nuclei after nuclear fusion

☐ **B** total mass of nuclei before nuclear fusion > total mass of nuclei after nuclear fusion

☐ **C** total mass of nuclei before nuclear fusion < total mass of nuclei after nuclear fusion

☐ **D** total mass of nuclei after nuclear fusion = 2 × total mass of nuclei before nuclear fusion

[1]

[Total 2 marks]

3 Two protons are fired at each other and combine to form a hydrogen-2 nucleus. **Grade 7-9**

Describe the conditions required for this reaction to occur and explain why they are needed.

....

....

....

....

[Total 3 marks]

Exam Practice Tip

When two things fuse, they join together. So fusion involves things joining together, and fission involves
something splitting apart. You might get a few marks by remembering that. Make sure you can explain why
nuclear fusion is so difficult to achieve — scientists haven't worked out how to use it for energy production yet.

Score

☐

___

6

Section 7 — Radioactivity and Particles

Section 8 — Astrophysics

The Universe

1 Which of the following correctly describes a galaxy? **Grade 3-4**

☐ **A** a star surrounded by orbiting planets

☐ **B** a collection of billions of stars

☐ **C** a collection of billions of universes

☐ **D** a collection of 5 to 10 stars

[Total 1 mark]

2 Earth is part of our Sun's solar system. **Grade 4-6**

a) State the name of the galaxy in which our solar system is found.

....

[1]

b) Approximately what shape are the orbits of the planets in our solar system?

....

[1]

c) The diagram below shows the Moon in orbit around the Earth. The direction of the Moon's instantaneous velocity is shown. Draw an arrow to show the direction of the force which keeps the Moon in orbit. Label the arrow you draw with the name of the force.

instantaneous
velocity

Moon

Earth

[2]

[Total 4 marks]

Exam Practice Tip

This is just one of those areas of physics where you need to learn a lot of words and facts I'm afraid.
So make sure you can remember what makes up a universe and a galaxy. You also need to be able to
explain how and why objects move in orbits around each other in space.

Score

☐

5

Gravity and Orbits

1   Which of the following correctly describes the typical shape of a moon's orbit?   (Grade 3-4)

- [ ] **A** helical
- [ ] **B** perfectly circular
- [ ] **C** slightly elliptical
- [ ] **D** highly elliptical

[Total 1 mark]

2   The diagrams below represent the orbits of four different objects in space.   (Grade 6-7)

a) Which of the objects, A, B, C or D, is most likely to be a comet? Explain your answer.

....

....

[2]

b) Objects A and D have the same time period and orbital radius. Object D has an orbital speed of 1.2 km/s. What is the orbital speed of object A? Give a reason for your answer.

....

....

[1]

c) Object B has an orbital radius of 42 000 km and a time period of 24 hours.
Calculate the orbital speed of object B.

Orbital speed = ... m/s

[3]

[Total 6 marks]

Section 8 — Astrophysics

3 A comet orbits a star with a varying orbital radius and speed. It completes one orbit in precisely 72 years and its orbital speed is 48.1 km/s at the fastest point in its orbit.

a) Calculate the time period of the comet's orbit in seconds. Assume there are 365 days in a year.

Time period = ... s

[1]

b) At which point in the comet's orbit will its speed be **greatest**? Explain your answer.

....

....

....

[2]

c) A planet travels in a circular orbit around the same star. It has the same orbital period as the comet and a constant orbital speed of 7.4 km/s. Calculate the orbital radius of this planet in metres.

Orbital radius = ... m

[3]

[Total 6 marks]

Score:

13

Stellar Evolution

1 The diagram below shows the life cycle of a star. (Grade 4-6)

Nebula   Protostar   Main sequence star   X   White dwarf

a) What is the name of the life cycle stage marked X?

☐ **A** red supergiant   ☐ **B** red giant   ☐ **C** red dwarf   ☐ **D** neutron star

[1]

b) State what is meant by a **nebula**.

....

[1]

c) Name the force responsible for 'pulling together' a nebula as it begins to form a star.

....

[1]

[Total 3 marks]

2 Betelgeuse is a star which is much more massive than our Sun. (Grade 6-7)

Describe the life cycle of a massive star like Betelgeuse, beginning from a cloud of dust and gas.

....

....

....

....

....

....

....

....

....

....

....

[Total 6 marks]

Score: ☐

9

Classifying Stars

1   The table below shows some properties of a number of stars. **Grade 4-6**

a)   Which of the following shows the stars
     in the correct order of hottest to coolest?

	Star	Absolute Magnitude	Colour
	Megrez	+1.3	White
	Pollux	+1.1	Orange
	Alkaid	−0.6	Blue

     ☐ **A** Megrez, Alkaid, Pollux

     ☐ **B** Alkaid, Pollux, Megrez

     ☐ **C** Pollux, Megrez, Alkaid

     ☐ **D** Alkaid, Megrez, Pollux

[1]

b)   State and explain which of the stars in the table is the brightest.

     ....

     ....

[2]

[Total 3 marks]

2   The diagram below shows the axes for a Hertzsprung-Russell diagram. **Grade 6-7**

Decreasing temperature

a)   State the variable displayed on the vertical-axis of the Hertzsprung-Russell diagram.

     ....

[1]

b)   Sketch the three main sections of a Hertzsprung-Russell diagram on the axes above.
     Label each section with the type of star they correspond to.

[4]

[Total 5 marks]

Exam Practice Tip

Classifying stars is important so that we can compare them and understand our universe better.
Make sure you know what the stars in the different classes have in common and how different properties of
stars are linked. For example, the colour of a star can tell you about its surface temperature.

Score

8

Section 8 — Astrophysics

Red-shift

1 When astronomers look at distant galaxies, they observe that the light coming from them has undergone red-shift.

Describe what is meant by the term **red-shift**.

....

....

[Total 2 marks]

2 An astronomer is analysing the light received from a distant galaxy, known as Hoag's Object.

To do this, she compares the absorption lines of helium observed in the light from Hoag's Object with the known absorption spectrum of helium on Earth. Part of the known absorption spectrum of helium is shown below.

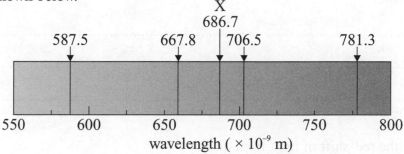

The astronomer notices that the absorption line for light with a reference wavelength, λ_0, of 587.5×10^{-9} m in the known spectrum appears to correspond to a wavelength of 612.5×10^{-9} m in the light received from Hoag's Object.

a) Calculate the velocity of Hoag's Object.

Speed of light in free space, $c = 3.0 \times 10^8$ m/s

Velocity = ... m/s

[3]

b) Calculate the wavelength at which the absorption line marked X in the spectrum above will appear in the light received from Hoag's Object.

Wavelength = ... m

[3]

[Total 6 marks]

Score:

8

Section 8 — Astrophysics

Paper 2

The Big Bang

1 The table shows a list of galaxies and their distance from Earth in light years. Grade 6-7

Galaxy	Distance From Earth (light years)
Cigar Galaxy	12 million
Black Eye Galaxy	24 million
Sunflower Galaxy	37 million
Tadpole Galaxy	420 million

1 light year ≈ 9.5 × 10¹⁵ m

The light from the galaxies in the table shows red-shift.

a) Light from which of the galaxies in the table would you expect to show the greatest red-shift? Explain your answer.

....

....

....

[3]

b) i) Explain how the red-shift of light from distant galaxies provides evidence for the Big Bang model.

....

....

....

....

....

....

....

[4]

ii) Name **one** other piece of evidence that supports the Big Bang model.

....

[1]

[Total 8 marks]

Exam Practice Tip

The Big Bang theory is the leading theory of the creation of the universe — but it wasn't always. It's only accepted because there's evidence to support it. Make sure you know the different observations which back up the Big Bang theory, and how the Big Bang theory explains them.

Score

8

Candidate Surname				Candidate Forename(s)	

Centre Number					Candidate Number			

Edexcel
International GCSE

Physics
Paper 1P

Practice Paper
Time allowed: 2 hours

You must have:
- A ruler.
- A calculator.

Total marks:

Instructions to candidates
- Use **black** ink to write your answers.
- Write your name and other details in the spaces provided above.
- Answer **all** questions in the spaces provided.
- In calculations, show clearly how you worked out your answers.
- You will need to answer some questions by placing a cross in a box, like this: ☒
  To change your answer, draw a line through the box like this: ☒
  Then mark your new answer as normal.

Information for candidates
- The marks available are given in brackets at the end of each question.
- There are 110 marks available for this paper.
- You might find the equations on page 156 useful.

Advice for candidates
- Read all the questions carefully.
- Write your answers as clearly and neatly as possible.
- Keep in mind how much time you have left.

Answer **all** questions

1   At the start of a roller coaster ride a carriage is raised by a chain lift through a vertical height
of 40 m to point W, as shown in the diagram. It is stopped at point W and then released to
follow the track through points X, Y and Z.

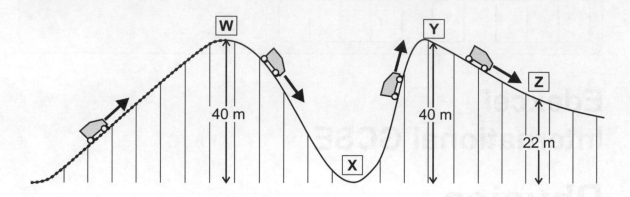

(a) (i)   At which two points does the carriage have the same amount of energy
in its gravitational potential energy store?

☐ **A**   X and Z

☐ **B**   W and Y

☐ **C**   Y and Z

☐ **D**   W and Z

[1]

(ii)   At which point does the car have the most energy in its kinetic energy store?

☐ **A**   W

☐ **B**   X

☐ **C**   Y

☐ **D**   Z

[1]

(b) The mass of the carriage and the people in it is 1500 kg.
The Earth's gravitational field strength is 10 N/kg.

(i) State the equation linking gravitational potential energy, mass, height and gravitational field strength.

....
[1]

(ii) Calculate the energy transferred to the gravitational potential energy store (in kJ) of a full carriage as it is raised by the chain lift to point W.

Energy = ... kJ
[2]

(c) (i) A different type of roller coaster uses a spring system to launch a carriage forward. State the energy store that energy is transferred from when a compressed spring is used to launch a roller coaster carriage.

....
[1]

(ii) State the equation linking efficiency, useful energy output and total energy output.

....
[1]

(iii) The spring system transfers 18.0 kJ of energy to the kinetic energy store of a carriage. However, the system also wastes 41.5 kJ of energy, transferred to useless thermal energy stores and carried away by sound. Calculate the efficiency of the spring system. Give your answer to an appropriate number of significant figures.

Efficiency = ... %
[3]

[Total 10 marks]

Turn over ▶

Practice Paper 1P

2   A swimmer swims one length of a 20 m swimming pool in a straight line.
The diagram below shows the distance-time graph of her motion.

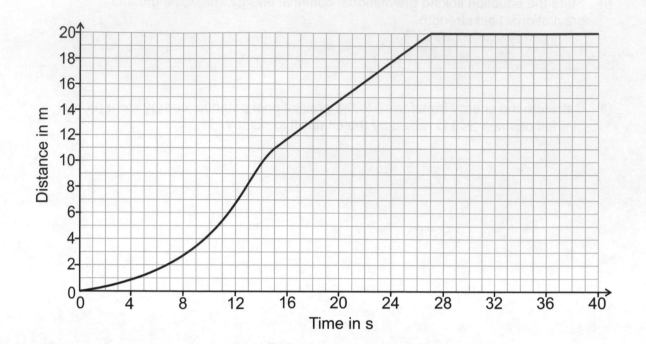

(a)   Determine the time it takes for the swimmer to complete the length.

Time = ... s

[1]

(b) (i)   For part of her swim, the swimmer is travelling at a constant speed.
Calculate the time she spends travelling at a constant speed.

Time = ... s

[1]

(ii)   State the resultant force on the swimmer when she is travelling
at a constant speed.

Force = ... N

[1]

(c)   Between which of the following **distances** was the swimmer travelling fastest?

☐ **A**   between 13 m and 14 m

☐ **B**   between 9 m and 10 m

☐ **C**   between 0 m and 1 m

☐ **D**   between 17 m and 18 m

[1]

A camera travels along the length of the pool to film the swimmer. It starts at the same time as the swimmer, travels at a constant speed, and reaches the end of the pool in 25 s.

(d) (i) State the equation which links speed, distance moved and time taken.

....
[1]

(ii) Calculate the speed of the camera.

Speed = ... m/s
[2]

(iii) On the diagram, draw a distance-time graph to represent the motion of the camera.
[2]

(e) The camera cannot film the swimmer if it is behind her.
Explain whether the camera will be able to film the swimmer for the whole length.
You should refer to the distance-time graphs in your answer.

....

....

....

....
[2]

[Total 11 marks]

3   A student wanted to model how the thickness of an insulating layer affects how quickly the content of a hot water tank cools. To model this system in the lab, she carried out an investigation to test how the thickness of a cotton wool jacket affected the rate of cooling of a beaker of hot water.
The apparatus she used is shown in the diagram below.

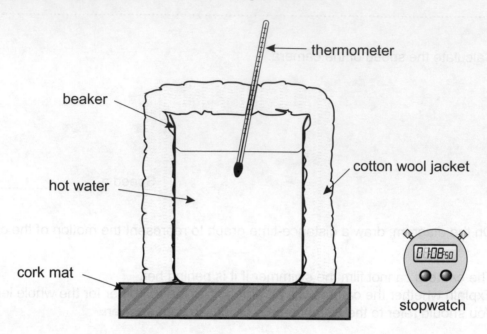

(a)   State the independent variable in this investigation.

....

[1]

(b)   State **one** control variable in this investigation.

....

....

[1]

(c)   The cotton wool jacket traps tiny pockets of air between the beaker and its surroundings.
Explain how this reduces the rate of energy transfer away from the beaker by convection.

....

....

[2]

(d)   The student decides to record the water's temperature after 3 minutes.
For each thickness of cotton wool jacket, she repeats this process three times.

(i)   Describe how the student could process her repeated results to get one value
for the final water temperature for each thickness of insulating layer.

....

....

[1]

(ii) The student's results are shown in the sketch below.

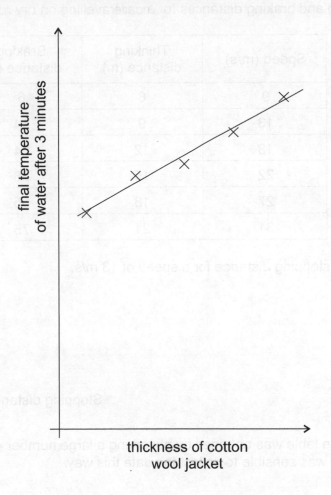

final temperature
of water after 3 minutes

thickness of cotton
wool jacket

Use the graph to write a suitable conclusion for this investigation.

....

....

[1]

[Total 6 marks]

4   A driving instructor has been looking at the Highway Code. He has found the following data about thinking and braking distances for a car travelling on dry roads at various speeds.

Speed (m/s)	Thinking distance (m)	Braking distance (m)
9	6	6
13	9	14
18	12	24
22	15	38
27	18	55
31	21	75

(a)   Calculate the stopping distance for a speed of 13 m/s.

Stopping distance = ... m

[1]

(b)   The data in the table was obtained by observing a large number of vehicles and drivers. Explain why it was sensible to collect the data this way.

....

....

....

[2]

(c)   Describe **three** different factors, other than speed, that can increase the stopping distance of a car. State whether each one affects the thinking distance or the braking distance.

1. ....

....

2. ....

....

3. ....

....

[5]

[Total 8 marks]

5 An artificial satellite orbits the Earth in an almost circular path, as shown in the diagram. It takes 1 day to orbit the Earth.

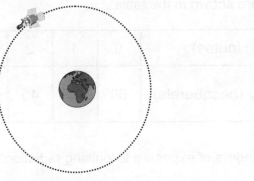

(a) Name the force that keeps the satellite in orbit around the Earth.

....

[1]

(b) The satellite has an orbital speed of 3080 m/s. Calculate the radius of the satellite's orbit.

Radius = ... m

[3]

The Earth orbits the Sun. Another planet that orbits the Sun is Venus.
The gravitational field strength on Venus is approximately 9 N/kg.

(c) Compare the weight of the same object on Venus and on Earth. Explain your answer.

....

....

....

[2]

The Sun is a main sequence star. Main sequence stars are fuelled by the nuclear fusion of hydrogen nuclei into helium nuclei. When the amount of hydrogen in the core of the Sun begins to run out, it will change into a different kind of star.

(d) Name the kind of star the Sun will become when it begins to run out of hydrogen in its core.

....

[1]

[Total 7 marks]

Turn over ▶

Practice Paper 1P

6 A student investigates a material that emits ionising radiation. He uses a detector to measure the activity of a sample of the radioactive material every minute.
His results are shown in the table.

Time (minutes)	0	1	2	3	4	5	6
Activity (becquerels)	80	60	45	34	25	19	14

(a) Give **two** dangers of exposure to ionising radiation.

1. ....

2. ....

[2]

(b) Suggest **one** piece of equipment that could have been used to measure the activity of the sample.

....

[1]

(c) (i) Plot the student's data on the grid below.

[3]

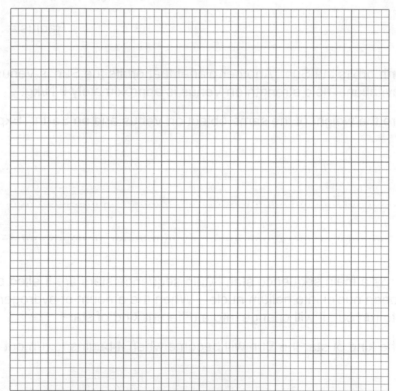

(ii) Draw a curve of best fit on the graph.

[2]

(iii) Use the graph to find the half-life of this radioactive material.

Half-life = ... min

[2]

(d)   After the experiment is finished, the radioactive sample is stored in another part of the building. The detector still picks up background radiation in the laboratory.

Give **one** source that may contribute to this background radiation.

....

....
[1]

(e) (i)   Another radioactive isotope, radium-226, decays by alpha emission.
Fill in the blanks in the reaction below to show the alpha emission.

$$^{226}_{88}\text{Ra} \quad \rightarrow \quad ^{222}_{.....}\text{Rn} \quad + \quad ^{.....}_{2}\alpha$$

[1]

(ii)   How many protons does the radium-226 (Ra) nucleus shown in part (i) have?

☐ **A**   226

☐ **B**   138

☐ **C**   88

☐ **D**   222

[1]
[Total 13 marks]

Turn over ▶

7   A student wanted to know how the current flowing through a filament lamp changes with the voltage across it. He set up this circuit.

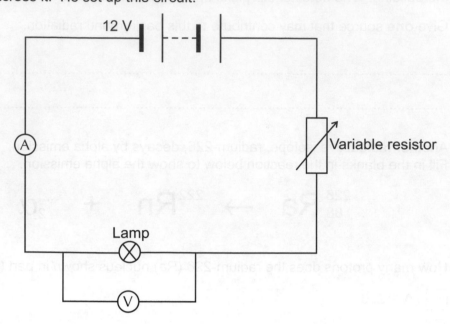

He used a variable resistor to change the voltage across the lamp.

Here is the graph he plotted of his results, along with his curve of best fit.

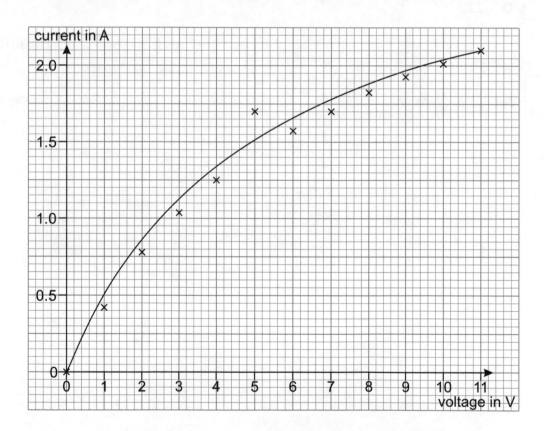

(a)   State the dependent variable in this experiment.

....

[1]

(b) (i) Describe what the student has done wrong when drawing the curve of best fit.

....

....
[1]

(ii) State the equation linking voltage, current and resistance.

....
[1]

(iii) The student corrects his curve of best fit and uses it to work out that when the voltage across the lamp is 5.0 V, the current through it is 1.4 A.
Calculate the resistance of the lamp when the voltage across it is 5.0 V.

Resistance = ... unit ....
[3]

(c) The student repeats the experiment with a fixed resistor in place of the filament lamp.
He again plots a graph of his results.

(i) Compare the shape of the graph the student would obtain for a fixed resistor with the graph for a filament lamp.

....

....
[1]

(ii) Explain why the shapes of these graphs are different.
You should refer to resistance in your answer.

....

....
[2]
[Total 9 marks]

8 An engineering student has made a simple electric motor as shown in the diagram.

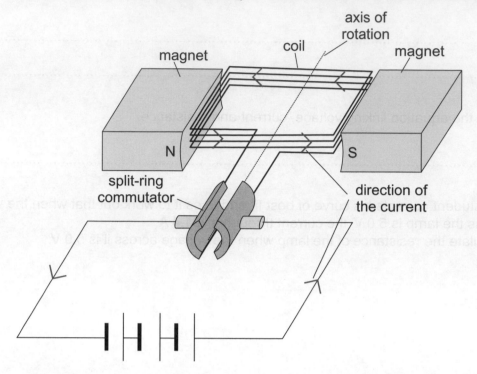

The split-ring commutator changes the direction of the current every half turn so that the motor will continue to rotate in the same direction.

(a) The direction of the current is shown. State which direction the coil will rotate in.

....

[1]

(b) Explain what makes the coil of wire in a simple electric motor rotate.

....

....

....

[2]

(c) The engineering student decides to make some changes to his motor.

Suggest **two** ways that he could speed up the rotation of the motor.

1. ....

....

2. ....

....

[2]

[Total 5 marks]

9   A hydraulic system is shown in the diagram below.

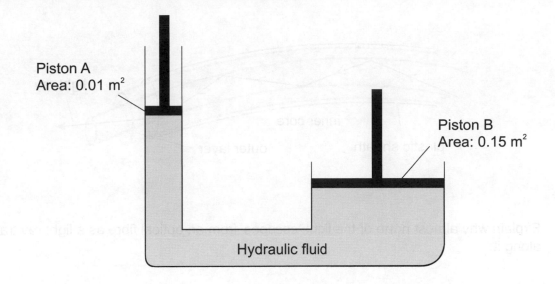

Piston A exerts a downwards force of 25 N.

(a)   Calculate the pressure in the liquid due to this force.

Pressure = ... Pa

[2]

(b)   Explain why there is a force on piston B when a force Is applied to piston A.

....

....

....

....

[3]

(c)   Show that the force on piston B is 375 N.

[2]

[Total 7 marks]

Turn over ▶

Practice Paper 1P

10   Optical fibres, such as the one shown below, are used in medicine.

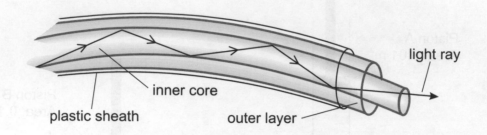

light ray

inner core

plastic sheath

outer layer

(a)   Explain why almost none of the light 'escapes' from an optical fibre as a light ray travels along it.

....

....

....

[2]

(b) (i)   Describe an experiment to find the refractive index of a rectangular block of the material used to make the inner core of an optical fibre.

....

....

....

....

....

....

[4]

(ii)   A student carries out the above experiment, using a laser as a light source. State **one** potential hazard involved with using a laser as a light source, and suggest **one** safety precaution that could be taken to minimise this hazard.

....

....

....

[2]

(c)   The refractive index of a material used to make optical fibres is 1.5. Light is shone into a semi-circular block of the material at different angles. As shown in the diagram, an angle, θ, is reached at which the light refracts along the flat boundary between the block and the air.

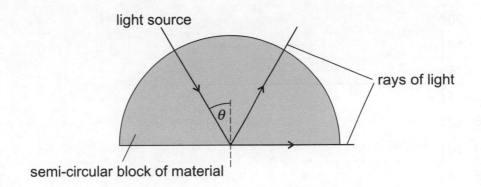

Calculate the angle θ.

$\theta = $ .... $^\circ$

[4]

[Total 12 marks]

11   This question is about velocity-time graphs.

(a)   The velocity-time graph below shows the motion of a vehicle as it travels along a flat, straight road before braking and stopping at a set of traffic lights.

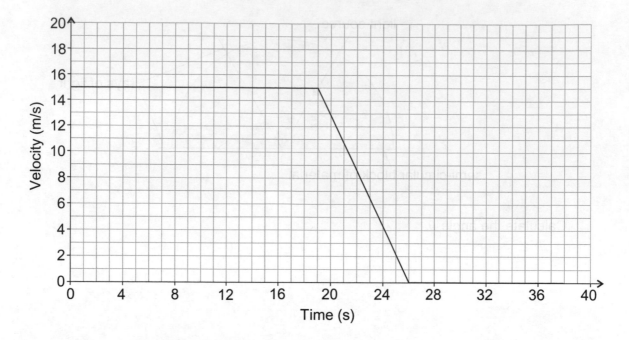

(i)   Calculate the total distance travelled by the car in the first 26 seconds.

Total distance travelled = ... m

[2]

(ii)   The vehicle has a mass of 1000 kg.
Calculate the size of the force applied by the brakes to bring the vehicle to a stop.

Force = ... N

[4]

(b)   The velocity-time graph below shows the motion of a skydiver jumping from an aeroplane.

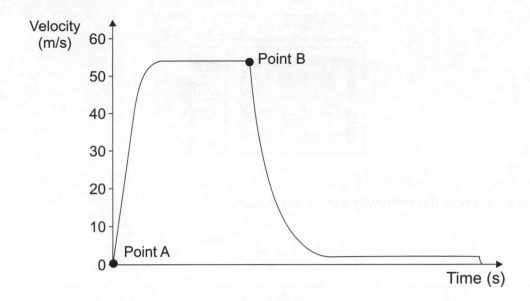

(i)   Describe the motion of the skydiver from point A to point B on the graph.
Your answer should refer to ideas about the forces acting on him.

....

....

....

....

....

....

[4]

(ii)   At point B, the skydiver opens his parachute.
Explain why this causes a change in his velocity.

....

....

....

[2]

[Total 12 marks]

12   A microwave oven can be used for heating food quickly.

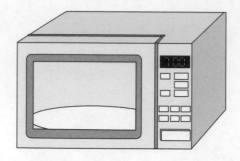

(a)   Describe how the microwave oven heats food.

....

....

....

....

[3]

(b) (i) State the equation linking frequency, wavelength and speed.

....

[1]

(ii) A microwave oven uses microwaves with a frequency of 2.5×10^9 Hz
that travel at 3.0×10^8 m/s. Calculate the wavelength of these microwaves.

Wavelength = ... m

[2]

(c) (i) Mobile phones work by transmitting and receiving microwave signals.
Explain why some people are concerned about using microwaves in this way.

....

....

....

[2]

(ii) Radio waves can also be used in communications technology.
Explain why radio waves have fewer potentially harmful effects than microwaves.

....

....

....

[2]

[Total 10 marks]

[Total for paper 110 marks]

Candidate Surname		Candidate Forename(s)	

Centre Number	Candidate Number

Edexcel
International GCSE

Physics
Paper 2P

Practice Paper
Time allowed: 1 hour 15 minutes

You must have:
- A ruler.
- A calculator.

Total marks:

Instructions to candidates
- Use **black** ink to write your answers.
- Write your name and other details in the spaces provided above.
- Answer **all** questions in the spaces provided.
- In calculations, show clearly how you worked out your answers.
- You will need to answer some questions by placing a cross in a box, like this: [x]
  To change your answer, draw a line through the box like this: [x̶]
  Then mark your new answer as normal.

Information for candidates
- The marks available are given in brackets at the end of each question.
- There are 70 marks available for this paper.
- You might find the equations on page 156 useful.

Advice for candidates
- Read all the questions carefully.
- Write your answers as clearly and neatly as possible.
- Keep in mind how much time you have left.

Answer **all** questions

1   The body panels of a plane are painted with a spray gun that gives the paint droplets a negative static charge. The body panels are given a positive static charge.

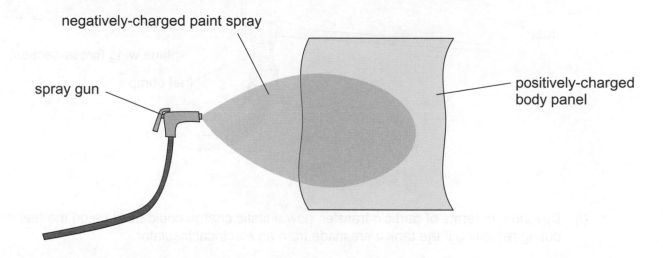

(a) (i)   The body panel is an electrical conductor.
Which of the following statements about electrical conductors is **incorrect**?

☐ **A**   Electrical conductors conduct charge easily.

☐ **B**   Metals are electrical conductors.

☐ **C**   Current can flow through electrical conductors.

☐ **D**   Plastic is an electrical conductor.

[1]

(ii) Explain why the spray gun produces a fine, even coverage of paint on the body panels, including areas that are not directly facing the spray gun.

....

....

....

....

....

....

[3]

Turn over ▶

Practice Paper 2P

(b)   When a plane is being refuelled, fuel is pumped into a tank in the wing of the plane. The tank and wing are made from metal and connected to earth.

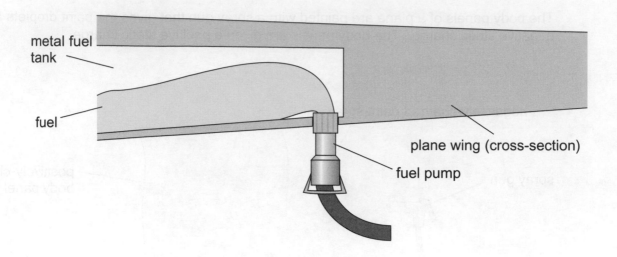

metal fuel tank

fuel

plane wing (cross-section)

fuel pump

(i)   Describe, in terms of particle transfer, how a static charge could build up on the fuel tank during refuelling if the tank were made from an electrical insulator.

....

....

....

....

....

[2]

(ii)   Explain why a build-up of static charge on the fuel tank could be dangerous.

....

....

[1]

[Total 7 marks]

2   Two skaters are taking part in a figure skating contest.
The diagram below shows their masses, and their velocities at one point in their routine.

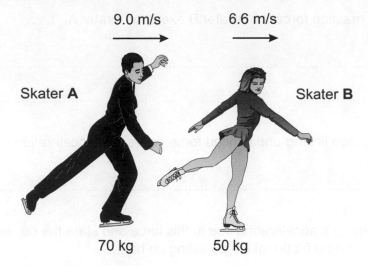

9.0 m/s   6.6 m/s

Skater **A**   Skater **B**

70 kg   50 kg

(a)   State the equation linking momentum, mass and velocity.

....

[1]

(b)   Complete the table below to show the momentum of each skater.

	Mass (kg)	Velocity (m/s to the right)	Momentum (kg m/s to the right)
Skater A	70	9.0	....
Skater B	50	6.6	....

[2]

(c)   The skaters continue at the same velocity until skater A catches up with skater B and holds on to her. They continue to move in the same direction.

Calculate their velocity immediately after skater A begins to hold skater B.

Velocity = ... m/s

[2]

Turn over ▶

(d) During the routine, the skaters come to a stop. Skater A then pushes skater B away from him with a force of 100 N.

(i) Describe the reaction force that skater B exerts on skater A.

....

....

[1]

(ii) State the equation linking unbalanced force, mass and acceleration.

....

[1]

(iii) Calculate skater B's acceleration due to this force and state the correct unit. Assume there are no frictional forces acting on her.

Acceleration = ... unit ....

[3]

[Total 10 marks]

3   The chart below shows the amount of electricity generated by different renewable energy resources in the UK each season between 2012 and 2015.
A kilowatt hour (kWh) is a unit of energy equal to 3.6×10^6 J.

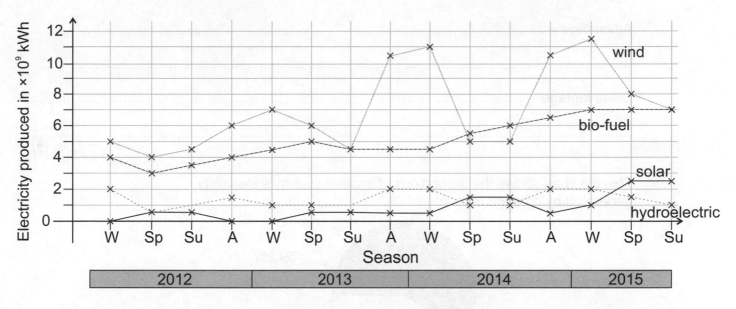

Key:

W — Winter   Sp — Spring   Su — Summer   A — Autumn

(a) (i)   Using the chart, determine the amount of electricity generated by bio-fuels and by hydroelectric power in summer 2014.

Bio-fuels = ... kWh

Hydroelectric = ... kWh

[2]

(ii)   Using the chart, suggest which renewable energy resource usually provides the largest amount of electricity to the UK.

....

[1]

(iii)   The chart shows that the amount of electricity generated from solar power during summer is always larger than the amount generated during winter of the same year.
Suggest a reason for this.

....

....

[1]

Turn over ▶

Practice Paper 2P

(b)   The majority of electricity in the UK is generated from non-renewable energy resources.
Give **one** advantage and **one** disadvantage of using non-renewable energy resources to
generate electricity.

Advantage = ...

....

Disadvantage = ...

....

[2]

This pie chart shows the proportions of another country's electricity
generated by different resources.

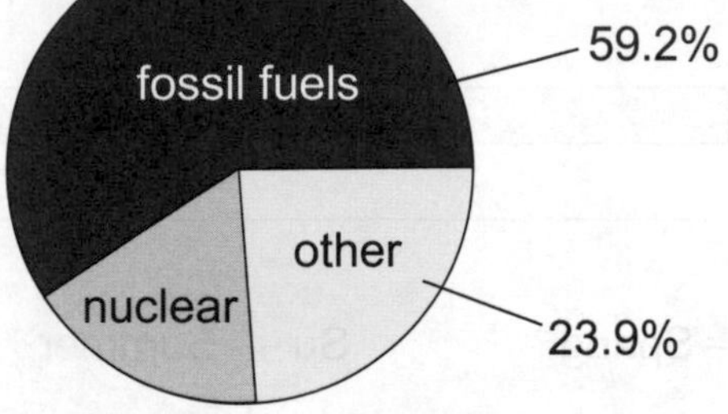

(c)   Calculate the proportion of the country's electricity that comes from nuclear power.

Proportion from nuclear power = ...%

[1]

(d)   Give **two** advantages and **two** disadvantages of using nuclear power to generate electricity
compared to burning fossil fuels.

Advantage = ...

....

Advantage = ...

....

Disadvantage = ...

....

Disadvantage = ...

....

[4]

[Total 11 marks]

4   A student performs an experiment to observe how the temperature of a solid
        changes when heated.

(a)   She places an electric heater in a hole in the solid and places a thermometer in a
        second hole. She turns the heater on and records the temperature every 100 seconds.
        Her results are shown in the table below.

Time (s)	Temperature (°C)
0	20.0
100	27.5
200	36.0
300	45.0
400	53.5
500	57.0
600	57.0

(i) Name **one** control variable in the student's experiment.

        ....
        [1]

(ii) Explain why control variables need to be kept constant in experiments such as this.

        ....

        ....
        [1]

Turn over ▶

Practice Paper 2P

(b) (i) Use the grid to plot a graph of the results in the table.

[3]

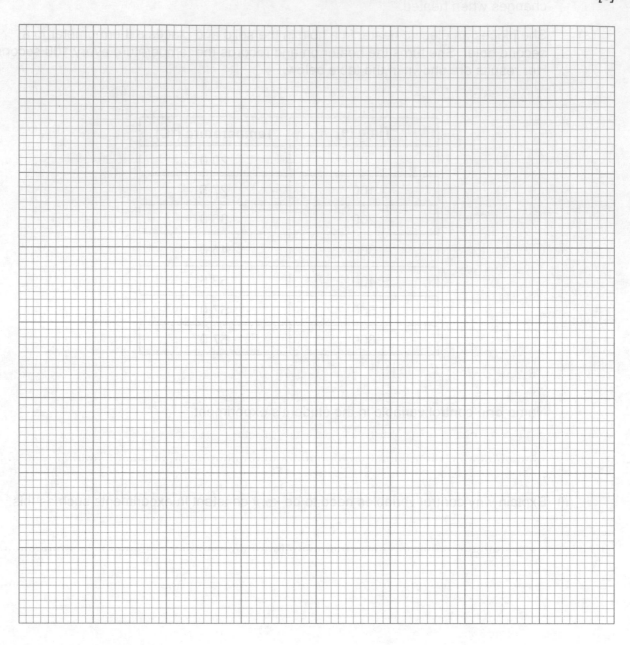

(ii) Draw a curve of best fit on the graph.

[2]

(c) The student looked up the heating curve for the material in a textbook.
She found the following graph.

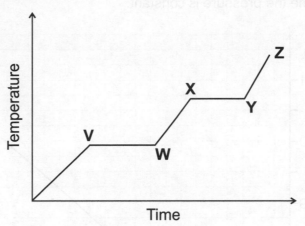

(i) Identify the state of matter of the substance at point **Z**.

....

[1]

(ii) Which point represents the **boiling point**?

☐ **A** V

☐ **B** W

☐ **C** X

☐ **D** Z

[1]

(iii) Explain the shape of the line between points **V** and **W**.

....

....

....

....

[2]

Turn over ▶

Practice Paper 2P

(d)   The student does another experiment where she steadily heats a gas in a container
with a changeable volume. She produces the following graph from her results.
You can assume the pressure is constant.

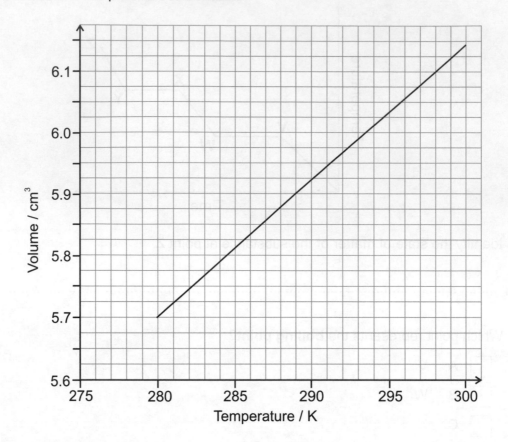

(i)   Using the graph, describe the relationship between the temperature and volume of the gas
at a constant pressure.

....

....

[1]

(ii) Use the graph to estimate the volume of the gas at 25 °C.

Volume of gas = ... cm³

[2]

[Total 14 marks]

5   The generator in a power station produces an alternating voltage of 25 kV.
This is changed to 400 kV by the transformer shown.

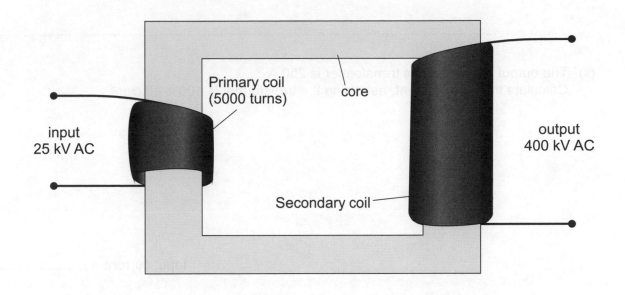

input
25 kV AC

Primary coil
(5000 turns)

core

Secondary coil

output
400 kV AC

(a)   State whether the transformer shown in the diagram is a step-up transformer
or a step-down transformer. Justify your answer.

....

....

[1]

(b) (i) State the equation linking the number of turns on the primary coil, the number of turns on
the secondary coil, the input voltage and the output voltage for a transformer.

....

[1]

(ii) The primary coil has 5000 turns.
Calculate the number of turns on the secondary coil.

Number of turns = ...

[3]

Turn over ▶

Practice Paper 2P

(c) (i) State the equation linking the input power and the output power in terms of the current and voltage across each coil of a 100% efficient transformer.

....

[1]

(ii) The output current of this transformer is 250 A.
Calculate the input current, assuming the transformer is 100% efficient.

Input current = ... A

[2]

(d) Explain why the electricity produced by power stations is passed through a transformer before being transmitted through the national grid.

....

....

....

....

....

[2]

[Total 10 marks]

6 A construction worker is using a crane with an electromagnet to pick up a metal load.

(a) State what is meant by an **electromagnet**.

....

....
[1]

(b) The electromagnet is shown in the diagram.

(i) Sketch magnetic field lines to show the shape of the magnetic field around the electromagnet.
[1]

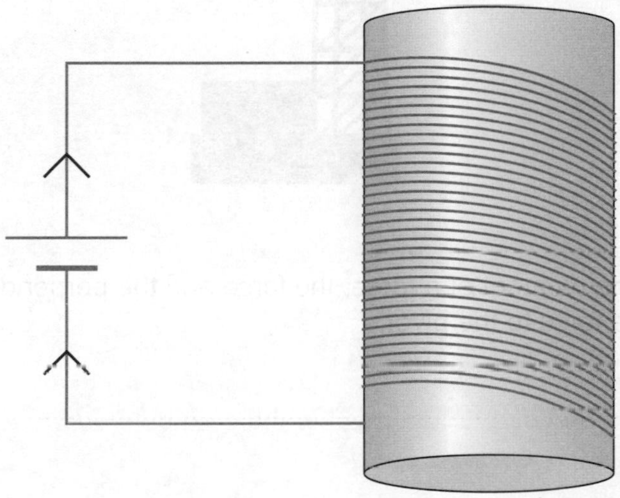

(ii) Explain why it is important for the core to be made from a magnetically soft material.

....

....
[1]

(c)   The diagram shows all the forces acting on the crane as it carries a metal anvil.
        The crane is balanced.

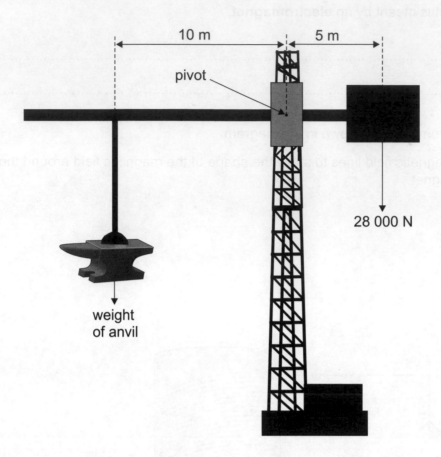

10 m   5 m

pivot

28 000 N

weight
of anvil

(i)   State the equation linking the moment of a force, the force and the perpendicular distance
        from the line of action of the force to the pivot.

        ....
        [1]

(ii)   Calculate the weight of the anvil using the information on the diagram.

        Weight = ... N
        [3]
        [Total 7 marks]

7   A student carried out an investigation into the specific heat capacity of liquids using the apparatus shown in the figure below. He used identical electric heating coils to heat a beaker of water and a beaker of oil. He used exactly 1 kg of each liquid.

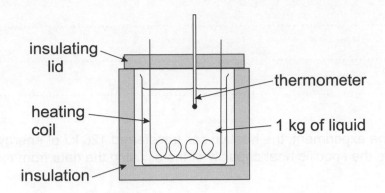

The student recorded the temperature of both the liquids before heating, and then again after ten minutes of heating. His results are shown in the table below.

	Water	Oil
Initial temperature in °C	18	18
Final temperature in °C	48	93

(a)   State what is meant by **specific heat capacity**.

....

....

[1]

(b)   The student used an insulating lid in the experiment.
State and explain the effect this has on the accuracy of the results.

....

....

[2]

Turn over ▶

(c)   Explain why the student uses the same mass of each liquid.

....

....

....

....
[2]

(d)   During the experiment, the heating coil transferred 126 kJ of energy to each liquid.
Calculate the specific heat capacity of the oil using the data from the experiment.

Specific heat capacity of oil = ... J/kg°C
[4]

(e)   Both oil and water can be used in heating systems.
Explain why most heating systems use water rather than oil.
You should refer to the specific heat capacities of oil and water in your answer.

....

....

....
[2]

[Total 11 marks]

[Total for paper 70 marks]

Answers

Section 1 — Forces and Motion

Pages 3-4 — Velocity and Acceleration

1 a) average speed = $\dfrac{\text{distance moved}}{\text{time taken}}$ / $v = \dfrac{s}{t}$ *[1 mark]*

b) $v = \dfrac{s}{t} = \dfrac{1500}{300} = \mathbf{5\ m/s}$

[2 marks if answer correct, otherwise 1 mark for correct substitution of values into the equation.]

c) $a = \dfrac{(v - u)}{t}$

$\Rightarrow t = \dfrac{(v - u)}{a} = \dfrac{(10 - 2)}{2.4} = 3.333... = \mathbf{3.3\ s}$ **(to 2 s.f.)**

[3 marks if answer correct, otherwise 1 mark for correct rearrangement of the equation and 1 mark for correct substitution of values into the equation.]

2 a) $v = \dfrac{s}{t} \Rightarrow s = v \times t = 0.46 \times 2.4 = 1.104 = \mathbf{1.1\ m}$ **(to 2 s.f.)**

[3 marks if answer correct, otherwise 1 mark for correct rearrangement of the equation and 1 mark for correct substitution of values into the equation.]

b) $a = \dfrac{(v - u)}{t} = \dfrac{78.4}{8.0} = \mathbf{9.8\ m/s^2}$

[2 marks if answer correct, otherwise 1 mark for correct substitution of values into the equation.]

3 a) Top speed of car = $v = \dfrac{s}{t} = \dfrac{180}{9} = 20\ m/s$

$a = \dfrac{(v - u)}{t} = \dfrac{20}{3.5} = 5.714... = \mathbf{5.7\ m/s^2}$ **(to 2 s.f.)**

[3 marks if answer correct, otherwise 1 mark for calculating top speed of car and 1 mark for correct substitution of values into the equation.]

b) $a = \dfrac{(v - u)}{t} \Rightarrow v = (a \times t) + u = (5.714... \times 1.5) + 0$

$= 8.571... = \mathbf{8.6\ m/s}$ **(to 2 s.f.)**

[3 marks if answer correct, otherwise 1 mark for correct rearrangement of the equation and 1 mark for correct substitution of values into the equation.]

You'll get full marks if an incorrect answer from part a) is used and the calculations are done correctly.

4 a) $v^2 = u^2 + 2as \Rightarrow u^2 = v^2 - 2as$

$\Rightarrow u = \sqrt{v^2 - 2as} = \sqrt{7^2 - (2 \times 2 \times 10)} = \mathbf{3\ m/s}$

[3 marks if answer correct, otherwise 1 mark for correct rearrangement of the equation and 1 mark for correct substitution of values into the equation.]

b) The tractor does accelerate. The tractor has changed direction, so there has been a change in velocity (and so there must have been an acceleration) *[1 mark]*.

Pages 5-6 — Distance-Time and Velocity-Time Graphs

1 a) 300 s *[1 mark]*

b) The student walks at a steady speed. The gradient of the graph shows the student's speed *[1 mark]* and the gradient for this part of the journey is constant (it's a straight line) *[1 mark]*.

c) speed = gradient = $\dfrac{\text{change in } y}{\text{change in } x} = \dfrac{450 - 0}{300 - 0} = \mathbf{1.5\ m/s}$

[2 marks if answer correct, otherwise 1 mark for correct substitution.]

d) E.g.

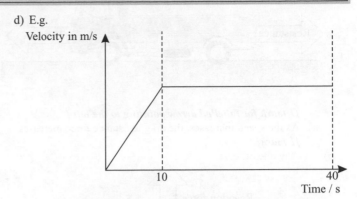

[3 marks available — 1 mark for a straight, sloped line showing the initial acceleration, 1 mark for a straight horizontal line showing the constant speed, and 1 mark for showing the times on the horizontal axis.]

2 a) i) Travelling at a steady velocity (20 m/s) *[1 mark]*.

ii) E.g. slowing down / (increasing) deceleration *[1 mark]*.

b) Distance travelled = area under graph

$= (60 - 40) \times (20 - 0)$

$= \mathbf{400\ m}$

[3 marks for the correct answer, otherwise 1 mark for attempting to find the area under the graph between 40 and 60 seconds, 1 mark for correctly showing (60 – 40) × 20 or 20 × 20.]

c) Acceleration = gradient = $\dfrac{20 - 0}{40 - 0} = \mathbf{0.5\ m/s^2}$

[3 marks for the correct answer, otherwise 1 mark for attempting to find the gradient, 1 mark for dividing a correct change in velocity by a correct change in time in the time range 0 – 40 s.]

d)

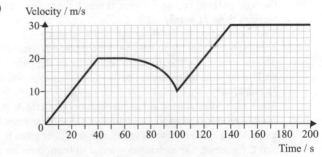

[1 mark for a straight line with a positive gradient between 100 and 140 seconds as shown, 1 mark for a straight horizontal line between 140 and 200 seconds.]

Page 7 — Mass, Weight and Gravity

1 a) i) Weight = mass × gravitational field strength / $W = m \times g$ *[1 mark]*

ii) $W = m \times g \Rightarrow g = \dfrac{W}{m} = \dfrac{19.6}{2}$

$= \mathbf{9.8\ N/kg}$ **(newtons per kilogram)**

[3 marks if answer correct, otherwise 1 mark for correct rearrangement of the equation and correct substitution of values into the equation, and 1 mark for correct unit.]

b) The weight would be smaller *[1 mark]* as the gravitational field strength, g, is lower on the Moon *[1 mark]*.

Page 8 — Forces and Friction

1 a) i)

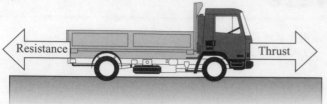

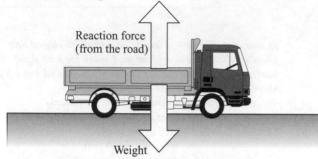

[1 mark for labelled arrow pointing to the left.]

ii) As the speed increases, the drag/resistance force increases *[1 mark]*.

b) Any one of: e.g.

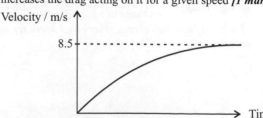

[1 mark for force label and 1 mark for direction.]
You could write "gravitational force" instead of "weight" here.

2 a) gravitational/weight *[1 mark]*

b) Increasing the drag acting on the plane lowers its speed *[1 mark]*. The parachute experiences a much higher drag than the plane, so releasing the parachute will increase the drag significantly, slowing the plane down *[1 mark]*.

Page 9 — Investigating Motion

1 a) Release the trolley so it can roll freely down the ramp and use the light gates to record the time at which the trolley passes through them *[1 mark]*.
The acceleration on the ramp can be found using acceleration = change in velocity ÷ time taken *[1 mark]*. The time taken for the trolley to accelerate on the ramp will be the time taken to pass between light gates A and B *[1 mark]*.
Since the trolley started at rest just before light gate A, its initial speed is 0 m/s and the change in velocity between light gates A and B is equal to its speed between light gates B and C (ignoring any slowing down due to friction on the flat runway) *[1 mark]*.
To find the trolley's speed on the runway, use the time taken for the trolley to pass from light gate B to light gate C, and the distance between them *[1 mark]*, to calculate the final speed of the trolley using average speed = distance moved ÷ time taken *[1 mark]*.

b) The student has changed two variables (distance and ramp angle) at the same time *[1 mark]*, so she cannot conclude which one caused the speed of the car to increase *[1 mark]*. She should measure the speed of the car when only the distance is changed, and separately measure the speed of the car when only the ramp angle is changed *[1 mark]*.

Pages 10-11 — The Three Laws of Motion

1 If object A exerts a force on object B then object B exerts an equal and opposite force on object A *[1 mark]*.

2 a) $F = m \times a$
For the Heath TT:
$F = m \times a = 950 \times 3 = 2850$ N
For the Asquith 380:
$F = m \times a = 790 \times 2 = 1580$ N
So the Heath TT has a greater maximum driving force.
[1 mark for calculating the maximum driving force of the Heath TT and 1 mark for calculating the maximum driving force of the Asquith 380.]

b) $F = ma \Rightarrow m = \dfrac{F}{a} = \dfrac{4000}{5} = \textbf{800 kg}$
[2 marks if answer correct, otherwise 1 mark for correct rearrangement of the equation and correct substitution of values into the equation.]

3 a) $F = m \times a \Rightarrow a = \dfrac{F}{m} = \dfrac{200}{2500} = \textbf{0.08 m/s}^2$
[2 marks if answer correct, otherwise 1 mark for correct rearrangement of the equation and correct substitution of values into the equation.]
Since the van is decelerating, you can include a minus sign in your answer.

b) i) $F = m \times a = 10 \times 29 = \textbf{290 N}$
[2 marks if answer correct, otherwise 1 mark for correct substitution of values into the equation.]

ii) 290 N *[1 mark]*

iii) $F = m \times a \Rightarrow a = \dfrac{F}{m} = \dfrac{290}{2500} = \textbf{0.116 m/s}^2$
[2 marks if answer correct, otherwise 1 mark for correct rearrangement of the equation and correct substitution of values into the equation.]
Since the van is decelerating, you can include a minus sign in your answer.

4 $F = m \times a$
The maximum force of the engine in each scooter ($= m \times a$)
$= 127.5 \times 2.4$
$= 306$ N
So, the mass of student B and her scooter $= \dfrac{F}{a}$
$= \dfrac{306}{1.70}$
$= \textbf{180 kg}$
[4 marks for correct calculation of the mass of student B and her scooter, otherwise 1 mark for stating that the maximum force is the same for each scooter, 1 mark for correct calculation of the maximum force and 1 mark for rearranging and substituting for the mass of student B and the scooter.]

Page 12 — Combining Forces

1 a) A scalar quantity just has size (magnitude) / is just a number *[1 mark]*. A vector quantity also has a direction *[1 mark]*.

b) D *[1 mark]*

c) A *[1 mark]*

2 a) Resultant force in the horizontal direction:
$1700 + 300 - 2000 = 0$ N
Resultant force in the vertical direction:
$800 - 300 = \textbf{500 N}$ *[1 mark]* **down** *[1 mark]*

b) i) $y - 400 = 0 \Rightarrow y = \textbf{400 N}$ *[1 mark]*

ii) $2000 - 500 - x = 0 \Rightarrow x = 2000 - 500 = \textbf{1500 N}$ *[1 mark]*

Page 13 — Terminal Velocity

1 a) When an object falls, its weight causes it to accelerate towards the ground *[1 mark]*. Resistive forces (e.g. air resistance) act on it in the opposite direction to its motion *[1 mark]*. As the object's speed increases, the resistive forces increase until eventually these balance the downward force of the object's weight *[1 mark]*. So there is no resultant force and it travels at a constant (terminal) velocity *[1 mark]*.

b) The patagium lowers the squirrel's terminal velocity as it increases the drag acting on it for a given speed *[1 mark]*.

c)

Velocity / m/s

8.5

Time

[1 mark for line drawn with gradient decreasing, 1 mark for line levelling off at 8.5 m/s.]

2   The ball with the lower weight, as it needs a smaller resistance/drag force to balance its weight *[1 mark]*. Air resistance increases with velocity *[1 mark]*, and the air resistance at any given velocity will be the same on each ball (because they're the same size), so air resistance will balance the weight at a lower velocity (giving a lower terminal velocity) *[1 mark]*.

If you answered the ball with the larger weight, you receive no marks for this question regardless of the reasoning.

Page 14 — Hooke's Law

1 a)

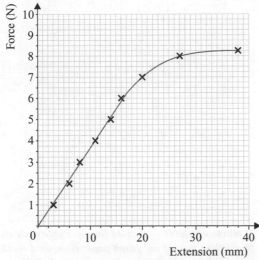

[3 marks available — 1 mark for all the points plotted correctly to within half a square, 1 mark for a suitable line of best fit passing through (0, 0) and 1 mark for line of best fit starting straight and curving after 18 mm. Deduct up to 2 marks, 1 mark for each incorrectly plotted point.]

b)   E.g.: They have a straight-line relationship / they are directly proportional to each other / Hooke's law is obeyed *[1 mark]*.

c)   No, it will not return to its original shape, because the spring's elastic limit has been passed *[1 mark]*.

Page 15 — Stopping Distances

1 a) i) Thinking distance *[1 mark]*.

   ii) Any two from: e.g.
tiredness / speed of the car / drug intake / alcohol intake / inexperience / old age.
[2 marks available — 1 mark for each correct answer.]

b) i) The distance the car travels during its deceleration whilst the brakes are being applied *[1 mark]*.

   ii) Any two from: e.g.
speed of the car / mass of the car / condition of the car's brakes / condition of the road surface / condition of the car's tyres / weather conditions.
[2 marks available — 1 mark for each correct answer.]

2 a)   E.g. rain reduces the grip of the tyres on the road *[1 mark]*, increasing the braking distance and stopping distance *[1 mark]*.

b)   E.g. decrease their speed *[1 mark]*

c)   stopping distance = thinking distance + braking distance
⇒ thinking distance = stopping distance – braking distance
= 37 – 28 = **9 m**
[2 marks if answer correct, otherwise 1 mark for correct substitution of values into the equation.]

Pages 16-18 — Momentum and Collisions

1 a) i) momentum = mass × velocity / $p = m \times v$ *[1 mark]*

   ii) $p = m \times v = 65 \times 14$
= **910 kg m/s (kilogram metres per second)**
[3 marks if answer correct, otherwise 1 mark for correct substitution of values into the equation and 1 mark for correct unit.]

b) i) force = $\dfrac{\text{change in momentum}}{\text{time taken}}$ / $F = \dfrac{(mv - mu)}{t}$ *[1 mark]*

   ii) force = $\dfrac{\text{change in momentum}}{\text{time taken}} = \dfrac{910}{1.3} = $ **700 N**
[2 marks if answer correct, otherwise 1 mark for correct substitution of values into the equation.]

You'll get full marks if an incorrect answer from part a) is used and the calculations are done correctly.

2   initial momentum of skater = 60 × 5 = 300 kg m/s
initial momentum of bag = 0
momentum of skater and bag = (60 + mass_bag) × 4.8
momentum before = momentum after
⇒ 300 = (60 + mass_bag) × 4.8
⇒ mass_bag = $\dfrac{300}{4.8}$ – 60 = **2.5 kg**
[5 marks if answer correct, otherwise 1 mark for equating momentum before and after, 1 mark for correct substitution of values to calculate the initial momentum of the skater, 1 mark for correct rearrangement of the equation, and 1 mark for correct substitution of values into the equation to find the momentum of the skater and bag.]

3 a) $p = m \times v = 650 \times 15$
= **9750 kg m/s**
[2 marks if answer correct, otherwise 1 mark for correct substitution of values into the equation.]

b)   momentum before = momentum after
$[m_1 \times v_1] + [m_2 \times v_2] = [(m_1 + m_2) \times v_{after}]$
$[650 \times 15] + [750 \times -10] = [(650 + 750) \times v_{after}]$
$9750 - 7500 = 1400 \times v_{after}$
$v_{after} = \dfrac{2250}{1400}$
$v_{after} = 1.607... = $ **1.6 m/s (to 2 s.f.)**
[4 marks if answer correct, otherwise 1 mark for equating momentum before and after, 1 mark for correct substitution of values into the equations for momentum of each vehicle and 1 mark for correct rearrangement of the equation(s).]

You'll get full marks if an incorrect answer from part a) is used and the calculations are done correctly.

c)   The crumple zone increases the time taken by the car to stop/change its velocity *[1 mark]*. The time over which momentum changes is inversely proportional to the force acting, so this reduces the force *[1 mark]*.

4 a) i) $p = m \times v = 410 \times 2.0 = $ **820 kg m/s**
[2 marks if answer correct, otherwise 1 mark for correct substitution of values into the equation.]

   ii) Total momentum before collision
= 820 – 484 = **336 kg m/s** *[1 mark]*

b) i) 336 kg m/s *[1 mark]*

   ii) Total momentum after collision = total momentum before collision, so 410 × (–1.2) + 440v = 336,
or –492 + 440v = 336.
So 440v = 336 + 492 = 828, which means
v = 828 ÷ 440 = 1.881... = **1.9 m/s (to 2 s.f.)**
[3 marks if answer correct, otherwise 1 mark for correct substitution of values into the equation and 1 mark for correct rearrangement of the equation.]

Page 19 — Turning Effects and Centre of Gravity

1   The point through which the object's weight acts *[1 mark]*.

2 a)   The turning effect of a force *[1 mark]*.

b)   B *[1 mark]* — the force is acting at the furthest perpendicular distance from the pivot *[1 mark]*.

c)   moment = force × perpendicular distance from the pivot
= 45 × 0.1 = **4.5 Nm (newton metres)**
[3 marks if answer correct, otherwise 1 mark for correct substitution of values into the equation and 1 mark for correct unit.]

Page 20 — Principle of Moments

1 a) 20 cm = 0.2 m

moment = force × perpendicular distance from the pivot
= 2 × 0.2 = **0.4 Nm**

[3 marks if answer correct, otherwise 1 mark for using the correct equation and 1 mark for correct substitution of values into the equation.]

b) clockwise moments about pivot = anticlockwise moments about pivot

$force_C$ × perpendicular $distance_C$ = 0.4 + 0.8

perpendicular $distance_C = \dfrac{0.4 + 0.8}{8} = $ **0.15 m**

[4 marks if answer correct, otherwise 1 mark for reference to balanced moments in each direction, 1 mark for correct substitution of values into the equation and 1 mark for correct rearrangement of the equation.]

You'll get full marks if an incorrect answer from part a) is used and the calculations are done correctly.

2 Situation B. Rope 1 balances the moment applied by the box around rope 2 *[1 mark]* and so the further the box is from rope 2, the larger the force applied by rope 1 *[1 mark]*.

Award no marks for this question if you answered situation A.

Section 2 — Electricity

Page 21 — Circuits — The Basics

1 a) A *[1 mark]*

b) Direct current *[1 mark]*. This means that the current keeps flowing in the same direction *[1 mark]*.

2 a)

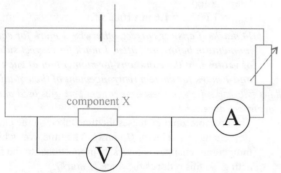

[1 mark for adding the ammeter in line with component X, 1 mark for adding the voltmeter across component X]

b) It will decrease *[1 mark]*.

c) E.g. start with the resistance of the variable resistor fixed at a high level. Then take a reading of current from the ammeter *[1 mark]* and voltage from the voltmeter *[1 mark]*. Decrease the resistance of the variable resistor in equal steps and take another pair of readings each time *[1 mark]*. Be sure to take several pairs of readings *[1 mark]*.

With these sorts of questions, you just need to make sure you get all the key points down. You could pick up some of the marks for saying things like the student should take repeats of all the readings and take averages, or for describing how they can make it a fair test.

Pages 22-23 — Resistance and V = I × R

1 D *[1 mark]*

2 a) (resistor) D *[1 mark]*

The graph with the shallowest slope corresponds to the component with the highest resistance.

b) i) Voltage = current × resistance / $V = I \times R$

[1 mark — accept any rearranged version of the same equation.]

ii) Choose a point on the line and use values of I and V to find R using $V = I \times R$. E.g. $I = 4$ A, $V = 2$ V

$R = \dfrac{V}{I} = \dfrac{2}{4} = $ **0.5 Ω**

[3 marks for correct answer, otherwise 1 mark for correct rearrangement and 1 mark for correct substitution.]

Using the values of I and V for any point on the line for component B should give you the same correct answer.

iii) $V = I \times R$ so $I = \dfrac{V}{R} = \dfrac{15}{0.75} = $ **20 A**

[3 marks for correct answer, otherwise 1 mark for correct rearrangement and 1 mark for correct substitution.]

3 a) A diode/LED *[1 mark]* because the current only flows in one direction *[1 mark]*.

b)

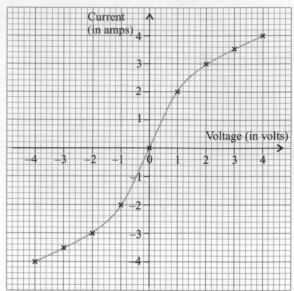

[4 marks available — 1 mark for a suitable scale chosen (more than half of the graph paper is used), 1 mark for a suitable line of best fit passing through (0, 0), 1 mark for the axes correctly labelled with quantities and units, 1 mark for all the points plotted correctly to within half a square. Deduct up to 2 marks, 1 mark for each incorrectly plotted point.]

c) i) (metal filament) lamp / bulb *[1 mark]*

ii) As the current through the filament of the lamp increases, the temperature increases *[1 mark]*. The temperature increase causes the resistance to increase *[1 mark]*. So less current can flow per unit of voltage, causing the graph to curve *[1 mark]*.

Page 24 — LDRs, Thermistors and LEDs

1 a) If the LED is lit up, current is flowing in the circuit *[1 mark]*.

b) The resistance increases *[1 mark]* because the resistance of a light dependent resistor increases with decreasing light intensity *[1 mark]*.

2 a) i) C *[1 mark]*

ii) A *[1 mark]*

b) i) E.g.

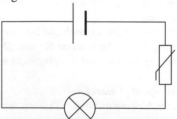

[3 marks available for a circuit diagram showing a circuit that will work containing a thermistor, a power source and a lamp, otherwise 1 mark for an incorrect but complete circuit containing 3 components including a lamp, 1 mark for drawing a thermistor in a complete circuit.]

ii) The current increases *[1 mark]*. As the temperature in the room increases, the resistance of the thermistor (and so the circuit) will decrease *[1 mark]*.

Answers

Page 25 — Series and Parallel Circuits

1 a) E.g. if one bulb breaks, the other still lights up *[1 mark]*.

b) $V = I \times R \Rightarrow R = \dfrac{V}{I} = \dfrac{12}{0.5} = \textbf{24 }\boldsymbol{\Omega}$

[3 marks for correct answer, otherwise 1 mark for correct rearrangement and 1 mark for correct substitution.]

c) It would decrease *[1 mark]*.

2 a) $V_1 = 4.2$ V
$V_2 = 4.2$ V *[1 mark]*

In parallel circuits, the potential difference is the same across all branches.

b) The current through a component depends on the total potential difference and the total resistance across all the components in series with it.

Total resistance across branch = $R_1 + R_2 = 2.0 + 2.0 = 4.0\ \Omega$

$V = I \times R \Rightarrow I = \dfrac{V}{R} = \dfrac{4.2}{4.0} = \textbf{1.05 A}$

[4 marks for correct answer, otherwise 1 mark for calculating resistance, 1 mark for correct rearrangement and 1 mark for correct substitution.]

Page 26 — Charge, Voltage and Energy Change

1 a) i) Rate of flow of (electrical) charge *[1 mark]*.

ii) (negatively charged) electrons *[1 mark]*.

b) i) Charge = current × time / $Q = I \times t$

[1 mark — accept any rearranged version of the same equation.]

ii) Convert time to seconds, $t = 20 \times 60 = 1200$ s
$Q = I \times t = 5 \times 1200 = \textbf{6000 C}$

[3 marks for correct answer, otherwise 1 mark for calculating the time in seconds and 1 mark for correct substitution.]

c) 3 J *[1 mark]*. Energy transferred per unit charge is equal to voltage, and the battery has a voltage of 3 V or 3 J/C *[1 mark]*.

d) $I = \dfrac{Q}{t} = \dfrac{12}{3.0} = 4.0$ A

$E = QIR \Rightarrow R = \dfrac{E}{QI} = \dfrac{36}{12 \times 4.0} = \textbf{0.75 }\boldsymbol{\Omega}$

[4 marks for the correct answer, otherwise 1 mark for calculating the current, 1 mark for correct rearrangement and 1 mark for correct substitution.]

Pages 27-28 — Electrical Safety

1 a) To protect the wiring of the house / prevent fires in the event of a fault *[1 mark]*.

b) Because pennies won't melt like a fuse wire in the event of a current surge, so the circuit won't be broken *[1 mark]*.

2 a) If the live wire comes loose and touches the metal, the current will flow away through the earth wire *[1 mark]*. The earth wire has a low resistance, so a large current flows through it, the live wire and the fuse *[1 mark]*. This current melts the thin wire in the fuse *[1 mark]*, cutting off the electricity supply to the toaster *[1 mark]*.

b) The kettle is double insulated. / Plastic is an (electrical) insulator *[1 mark]*. This means the casing doesn't conduct electricity, so it can never become live *[1 mark]*.

3 a) i) E.g. the metal casing can become live and give someone an electric shock if they touch it *[1 mark]*.

ii) A large current surges to earth through the earth wire *[1 mark]*. This causes a large current to surge through the live wire and trip the circuit breaker *[1 mark]*. The circuit breaker breaks the circuit and isolates the microwave oven *[1 mark]*.

b) i) A fuse melts to break a circuit *[1 mark]* whereas a circuit breaker opens a switch to break a circuit *[1 mark]*.

ii) Any two of: e.g. circuit breakers don't need to be replaced every time they break the circuit/can be easily reset. / Some circuit breakers operate much faster than a fuse, making them safer. / Some circuit breakers can detect and respond to much smaller (but still dangerous) current changes than a fuse.

[2 marks — 1 mark for each correct advantage.]

Page 29 — Energy and Power in Circuits

1 a) When current flows through the wire, the charges do work against the resistance and energy is transferred to thermal energy stores *[1 mark]* and the higher the resistance, the more energy is transferred *[1 mark]*.

b) i) Power = current × voltage / $P = I \times V$

[1 mark — accept any rearranged version of the same equation.]

ii) Convert power to W, $P = 2.8 \times 1000 = 2800$ W

$I = \dfrac{P}{V} = \dfrac{2800}{230} = 12.17\ldots$ A = **12 A (to 2 s.f.)**

[3 marks for correct answer, otherwise 1 mark for correctly converting power to W and 1 mark for correctly substituting into a correctly rearranged equation.]

iii) D *[1 mark]*

Remember that fuses should be rated as near as possible but just higher than the normal operating current, which is 12 A here.

iv) She should choose kettle B because it has the higher power rating *[1 mark]*. This means that it transfers more energy per unit time, so it will boil the water faster *[1 mark]*.

Page 30 — Static Electricity

1 a) A material that doesn't conduct charge/electricity very well *[1 mark]*.

b)

Material	Electrical conductor?	Electrical insulator?
Glass	No	Yes
Water	Yes	No
Plastic	No	Yes
Copper	Yes	No

[2 marks, 1 mark for each correct row.]

2 a) The man is charged, so there is a potential difference/voltage between him and the rail *[1 mark]*. When the potential difference/voltage is high enough, electrons jump across the gap to the rail, producing a spark *[1 mark]*.

b) Negatively charged *[1 mark]*. Only negative charges/electrons can move *[1 mark]* and they will move from an area of negative charge to an earthed area *[1 mark]*.

Pages 31-32 — Static Electricity and Friction

1 a) Electrons are removed from the dusting cloth *[1 mark]* and transferred to the polythene rod *[1 mark]*.

b) Bring the object with unknown charge near to the suspended polythene rod *[1 mark]*. If the rod moves away from / is repelled by the object, the object is negatively charged *[1 mark]*. If the rod moves towards / is attracted by the rod, the object is positively charged *[1 mark]*.

2 a) metal *[1 mark — accept any sensible named metal]*

b) Bring the material near to the disc of the electroscope *[1 mark]*. If the gold leaves rise, the material is charged. If they do not rise, the material is not charged *[1 mark]*.

c) No, the electroscope cannot distinguish between positive and negative charge. The charged object induces a charge in the metal disc, which induces a charge in the gold leaves *[1 mark]*. The charges on the gold leaves will always be alike *[1 mark]*, so the gold leaves will repel each other whether this charge is positive or negative *[1 mark]*.

3 a) Rubber is an insulator *[1 mark]* so the dome cannot discharge through the belt *[1 mark]*.

b) It needs to conduct charge so that electrons can flow from the dome to the belt, which leaves a positive charge on the dome *[1 mark]*.

c) The belt is positively charged and electrons are negatively charged and opposite charges attract *[1 mark]*.

d)   Negative charges move from the student's body to the dome, leaving unbalanced positive charges behind (including in the student's hairs) *[1 mark]*. Like charges repel *[1 mark]*, so the student's charged hairs stand on end (to get as far away from other charged hairs as possible) *[1 mark]*.

Pages 33-34 — Static Electricity — Examples

1   Rain drops and ice bumping together in clouds causes electrons to be transferred, causing the top and bottom layers of the cloud to become (oppositely) charged *[1 mark]*. This causes a big voltage between different parts of the cloud / between the (bottom of the) cloud and earth which may discharge through a spark (lightning) *[1 mark]*.

2 a)   It can cause a spark *[1 mark]*, which can cause a fire or an explosion if it ignites fuel or fuel fumes *[1 mark]*.

  b)   Make the nozzle out of metal *[1 mark]*. Connect the fuel nozzle to the fuel tank with an earthing strap *[1 mark]*.

3 a)   Inside the printer are two metal plates that can have a voltage applied to them *[1 mark]*. The voltage gives the plates opposite charges, which causes the droplets passing between them to be deflected, as they are attracted by one and repelled by the other *[1 mark]*. The amount and direction of deflection can be controlled by changing the size and direction of the voltage *[1 mark]*.

  b) i)   Light reflected off some parts (the white parts) of the original document onto the image plate *[1 mark]*.

    ii)   The black parts of the document don't reflect light onto the plate, so the image plate keeps its positive charge in those places *[1 mark]*. A negatively-charged black powder *[1 mark]* is brought close to the plate and attracted to the positively-charged parts of it *[1 mark]*. Then a positively-charged piece of paper *[1 mark]* is brought close to the plate and the negatively-charged black powder is attracted to the paper *[1 mark]*.

Section 3 — Waves

Pages 35-36 — Waves — The Basics

1 a)   Type A is a longitudinal wave, because the vibrations are in the same direction as/parallel to the direction of energy transfer *[1 mark]*. Type B is a transverse wave, because the vibrations are at 90° to the direction of energy transfer *[1 mark]*.

  b)   E.g. sound waves / ultrasound waves / shock waves *[1 mark]*

2 a)   2 Hz *[1 mark]*

  b) i)   wave speed = frequency × wavelength / $v = f \times \lambda$
[1 mark — accept any rearranged version.]

    ii) $v = f \times \lambda$ so $\lambda = \dfrac{v}{f} = \dfrac{0.5}{2} = \textbf{0.25 m}$
[2 marks for the correct answer — otherwise 1 mark for correctly rearranging the equation and substituting the correct values into the equation.]

Remember, the wavelength of a wave is the distance from crest to crest.

    iii) $f = \dfrac{1}{T}$, so $T = \dfrac{1}{f} = \dfrac{1}{2} = \textbf{0.5 s}$
[2 marks for the correct answer — otherwise 1 mark for correctly rearranging the equation and substituting the correct values into the equation.]

You still get full marks if an incorrect value from part a) is used correctly to calculate the period.

3 a)   E.g. the amplitude is the distance from the rest position of the wave to a crest *[1 mark]*.

  b)   C *[1 mark]*

c) i)   The wavelength — e.g. he has drawn a wavelength of 4 cm, not 2 cm *[1 mark]*.

  ii)   E.g.

height of the wave from
the rest position in cm

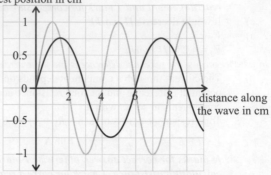

[2 marks available for drawing a correct wave — otherwise 1 mark for drawing a wave with the correct amplitude or the correct wavelength]

Page 37 — Wave Behaviour and EM Waves

1 a)   D *[1 mark]*

  b)   They don't travel faster than radio signals because all electromagnetic waves travel at the same speed in free space *[1 mark]*.

2 a)   The Doppler effect is the change in the observed frequency/wavelength of a wave *[1 mark]* due to the wave source moving towards or away from the observer *[1 mark]*.

  b)   Wave speed is constant, so a moving source can 'catch up' to the wavefronts of the waves produced in front of it *[1 mark]*. This causes the wavefronts in front of the source to bunch up, so the waves produced appear to have a shorter wavelength/higher frequency *[1 mark]*. The wavefronts behind the source spread out, so the waves produced appear to have a longer wavelength/lower frequency *[1 mark]*.

  c)   The distant star is moving away from the Earth *[1 mark]*. The Doppler effect causes frequencies emitted by a source moving away from a detector to seem lower than expected *[1 mark]*.

Pages 38-40 — Uses of Electromagnetic Waves

1 a)   gamma radiation *[1 mark]*.

  b)   Treating the fruit with radiation kills the microbes in it *[1 mark]*, which means that it will stay fresh for longer *[1 mark]*.

2   Microwaves are targeted at the food and absorbed by the water/fat molecules in the food *[1 mark]*. They penetrate a few centimetres into the food before being absorbed *[1 mark]*. The energy is then conducted or convected to other parts of the food *[1 mark]*.

3 a)   B *[1 mark]*

  b)   Data is carried as pulses of light *[1 mark]*. A pulse of light enters the narrow core of a fibre at a certain angle at one end and is reflected from the sides again and again until it emerges at the other end *[1 mark]*.

  c)   E.g. telephone and broadband internet cables / to see inside the body *[1 mark]*.

4   The fox is hotter than its surroundings, so it gives off more infrared radiation *[1 mark]*. The night vision camera detects how much infrared radiation objects give off and uses this to form an image *[1 mark]*.

5 a)   Long-wave: radio signals bend round the surface of the Earth to reach the house *[1 mark]*.
Short-wave: radio signals reflect off the ionosphere to reach the house *[1 mark]*.

b) i) microwave radiation *[1 mark]*
  ii) They are transmitted through the atmosphere into space, where they are picked up by a satellite receiver orbiting Earth *[1 mark]*. The satellite transmits the signal back to Earth in a different direction, where it is received by a satellite dish connected to the house *[1 mark]*.

6 a) A detector is placed behind the truck *[1 mark]*. The X-rays are absorbed by some objects *[1 mark]*, but are transmitted by others *[1 mark]*. A negative image is formed with brighter areas where fewer X-rays get through, indicating the objects that absorbed the X-rays *[1 mark]*.

  b) Exposure to X-rays can be harmful *[1 mark]*, so the driver and passengers should step outside the truck while it is exposed to X-rays to minimise their exposure *[1 mark]*.

7 a) They are not harmful. Almost all of the ultraviolet radiation is absorbed *[1 mark]* by a (phosphor) coating on the inside of the glass, which then emits visible light instead *[1 mark]*.

  b) A camera focuses light onto a light-sensitive film or electronic sensor *[1 mark]*. The camera can control how much light enters it by controlling how big the aperture is *[1 mark]*. The photographer can control how long the film or sensor is exposed to the light by changing the shutter speed *[1 mark]*.

Page 41 — Dangers of Electromagnetic Waves

1 a) Any two from: e.g. cell destruction *[1 mark]* / cancerous changes (mutations) to cells *[1 mark]* / tissue damage *[1 mark]*.

  b) E.g. keep exposure time to a minimum *[1 mark]* / place screening materials over doctors/other body parts in the vicinity of the gamma radiation *[1 mark]*.

2 a) Ultraviolet radiation can be ionising and cause (skin) cancer/ cell damage *[1 mark]*. Excessive sunbathing is dangerous because the more you are exposed to UV radiation, the more likely you are to be damaged by it *[1 mark]*.

  b) E.g. use sunscreen with ultraviolet filters / limit your exposure to the sun *[1 mark]*.

3 a) E.g. microwaves can cause internal heating of human body tissue *[1 mark]*.

  b) E.g. infrared also has a heating effect *[1 mark]*, but it has a higher frequency than microwaves and carries more energy (so it will have a greater heating effect) *[1 mark]*.

Page 42 — Reflection and Refraction of Waves

1 a) i) The angle of incidence is equal to the angle of reflection *[1 mark]*.

  ii) It is the reflection of light at all different angles when it reflects off an uneven surface *[1 mark]*.

  b) E.g.

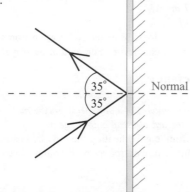

[1 mark for correctly drawn incident ray with an angle of incidence of 35°, 1 mark for correctly drawn reflected ray with an angle of reflection of 35°.]

  c) Waves travel at different speeds in materials with different densities *[1 mark]*. When a wave crosses a boundary into another medium at an angle, it changes direction *[1 mark]*. This is refraction *[1 mark]*.

Page 43 — More About Refraction of Waves

1 a) E.g.

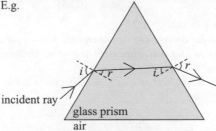

[1 mark for refracting the ray towards the normal upon entering the prism, 1 mark for refracting the ray away from the normal as it leaves the prism, and 1 mark for correctly labelling all the angles of incidence and refraction.]

  b) E.g. place the prism on a piece of paper and shine a ray of light at the prism. Trace the incident and emergent rays and the boundaries of the prism on the piece of paper *[1 mark]*. Remove the prism and draw in the refracted ray through the prism by joining the ends of the other two rays with a straight line *[1 mark]*. Draw in the normals *[1 mark]* and use a protractor to measure i and r *[1 mark]*.

  c) i) White light is made up of different colours of light *[1 mark]*, which have different wavelengths and so refract by different amounts at each boundary of the prism *[1 mark]*.

  ii) The sides of a rectangular block are parallel *[1 mark]*, and so the rays of different colours of light bend by the same amount but in opposite directions when they enter and leave the block so they emerge parallel *[1 mark]*.

Pages 44-45 — Refractive Index and Snell's Law

1 a) E.g.

[1 mark for a suitable scale chosen (more than half of the graph paper is used), 1 mark for a suitable line of best fit passing through (0, 0), 1 mark for the axes labelled with quantities and scales, 1 mark for correctly plotted points. Deduct up to 2 marks for incorrectly plotted points, 1 mark per incorrect point.]

  b) i) gradient = $\dfrac{\text{change in } y}{\text{change in } x}$

  e.g. gradient = $\dfrac{0.5 - 0}{0.6 - 0} = 0.833... = $ **0.833 (to 3 s.f.)**

  [2 marks for correct answer, otherwise 1 mark for correct substitution.]

You could calculate your gradient using any correct pair of points on your graph. You'd get the marks here as long as your answer is correct for your graph and line of best fit from part a).

ii) gradient $= \dfrac{1}{n}$, so $n = \dfrac{1}{\text{gradient}} = \dfrac{1}{0.833...} = 1.2$

So refractive index = **1.2**

[2 marks for correct answer, otherwise 1 mark for correct substitution and rearrangement to find n. Deduct 1 mark for giving units.]

Again, you'd get the marks here as long as your answer is correct for the answer you gave in part i).

2 a) $i = 45°$

$n = \dfrac{\sin i}{\sin r}$ so $\sin r = \dfrac{\sin i}{n} = \dfrac{\sin 45.0°}{1.514} = 0.467...$

So $r = \sin^{-1}(0.467...) = 27.8426... = $ **27.8°** (to 3 s.f.)

[3 marks for correct answer, otherwise 1 mark for correct substitution and 1 mark for correct rearrangement.]

b) The separation happens when different colours refract by different amounts *[1 mark]*, but light doesn't refract when it crosses a boundary along the normal *[1 mark]*.

c) Angle of incidence for violet light = $i = 45.0°$

$\sin r = \dfrac{\sin i}{n} = \dfrac{\sin 45.0°}{1.528} = 0.4627...$

$\Rightarrow r = \sin^{-1}(0.4627...) = 27.5657...°$

Then subtract this angle from the angle of refraction of red light to get:

$\theta = 27.8426... - 27.5657... = 0.2769... = $ **0.277°** (to 3 s.f.)

[4 marks for correct answer, otherwise 1 mark for correct rearrangement of the equation to find r, 1 mark for correct angle of refraction of violet light and 1 mark for correctly subtracting one angle from the other.]

You get the marks here if the answer given to part a) is used correctly (even if it's wrong).

Page 46 — Refractive Index and Critical Angles

1 a) $\sin C = \dfrac{1}{n} \Rightarrow C = \sin^{-1}\left(\dfrac{1}{n}\right) = \sin^{-1}\left(\dfrac{1}{1.54}\right) = 40.492...$
$= $ **40.5°** (to 3 s.f.)

[3 marks for correct answer, otherwise 1 mark for correct substitution and 1 mark for correct rearrangement.]

b) Bending an optical fibre sharply may result in some light meeting the boundary at an angle that is smaller than or equal to the critical angle *[1 mark]*. This means light will escape the optical fibre, so less light will be used to make the image *[1 mark]*.

2 a) E.g. the angle of incidence such that the angle of refraction is 90° (for light travelling from a denser material to a less dense material) *[1 mark]*.

b) It will be reflected back into the acrylic (total internal reflection) *[1 mark]*.

c) $n = \dfrac{1}{\sin C} = \dfrac{1}{\sin 41.8°} = 1.5003... = $ **1.50** (to 3 s.f.)

[3 marks for correct answer, otherwise 1 mark for using the correct equation and 1 mark for substituting correct values into the equation. Deduct 1 mark for giving units.]

Pages 47-48 — Sound Waves

1 a) i)

Statements	Order
Measure the distance between the microphones. This is the wavelength.	4
Stop moving microphone 2 when the traces line up.	3
Use the measured distance and the frequency of the signal generator to find the wave speed.	5
Begin with both microphones at an equal distance from the speaker.	1
Keeping microphone 1 fixed, slowly move microphone 2 away from the speaker (keeping it in line with microphone 1), causing trace 2 to move.	2

[3 marks for all entries correct, 2 marks if two entries correct, and 1 mark if one entry correct.]

ii) $v = f \times \lambda = 50 \times 6.8 = $ **340 m/s**

[2 marks for correct answer, otherwise 1 mark for substituting correct values into the equation.]

b) i) D *[1 mark]*

ii) One time cycle is 8 divisions long, so $T = 0.005 \times 8 = 0.04$ s

$f = \dfrac{1}{T} = \dfrac{1}{0.04} = $ **25 Hz**

[2 marks for correct answer, otherwise 1 mark for substituting correctly into correct equation.]

iii) E.g.

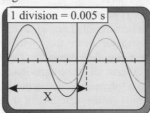

1 division = 0.005 s

[1 mark for increasing the amplitude of the wave. Award no marks if the time period of the wave has changed.]

2 a) The echoes are caused by the reflection of sound waves from the surfaces of the drama hall and on the field there are no walls for the waves to reflect off *[1 mark]*.

b) E.g. it may refract (change direction) *[1 mark]*.

c) i) 20 – 20 000 Hz *[1 mark]*

ii) The frequency is lower *[1 mark]*. This is because the pitch of his voice is lower and frequency determines pitch *[1 mark]*.

d) The female student, as it has a higher frequency/shorter time period, which corresponds to a higher pitch *[1 mark]*.

Section 4 — Energy Resources and Energy Transfer

Page 49 — Conservation of Energy

1

Scenario	Energy Transferred From...
A skydiver falling from an aeroplane.	gravitational potential energy store
A substance undergoing a nuclear reaction.	nuclear energy store
A stretched spring returning to its original shape.	elastic potential energy store
A piece of burning coal.	chemical energy store

[3 marks for all correct, otherwise 2 marks for 2 correct or 1 mark for 1 correct]

2 a) thermal *[1 mark]*

b) D *[1 mark]*

c) Energy can be stored, transferred between stores or dissipated *[1 mark]* but it can never be created or destroyed *[1 mark]*.

Page 50 — Efficiency

1 D *[1 mark]*

They all have the same amount of input energy, so the most efficient is the one with the largest amount of useful output energy.

2 a) Any one from: e.g. by heating the fan / by heating the surroundings / transferred away by sound waves *[1 mark]*.

b) total energy input = total energy output

2 kJ = 2 × 1000 = 2000 J

Find the energy that is transferred usefully:

useful energy output = total energy output – wasted energy

= 7250 – 2000 = 5250

$\text{efficiency} = \frac{\text{useful energy output}}{\text{total energy output}} \times 100\%$

$= \frac{5250}{7250} \times 100\% = 72.413...\ \% = \textbf{72 \%}$ (to 2 s.f.)

[4 marks for correct answer, otherwise 1 mark for correct conversion, 1 mark for correctly calculating the useful output energy, 1 mark for correctly calculating the efficiency and 1 mark for giving your answer to 2 s.f.]

3   D *[1 mark]*

The mains transfers 2500 J/s, but the kettle is only 76% efficient. So 2500 × 0.76 = 1900 J/s is usefully transferred to the thermal energy store of the water. 418 000 J is needed to boil the water, so it takes 418 000 ÷ 1900 = 220 seconds.

Page 51 — Energy Transfers

1   C *[1 mark]*

2 a) Energy is transferred mechanically from the chemical energy stores of the weight lifter's muscles *[1 mark]* to the kinetic energy stores of his arms and the weights *[1 mark]*. Some of this energy is transferred mechanically from the kinetic energy stores to the gravitational potential energy store of the weights *[1 mark]*.

   b) Energy is transferred mechanically from the gravitational potential energy store of the weights *[1 mark]* to their kinetic energy store *[1 mark]*.

3   The golf club has energy in its kinetic energy store *[1 mark]*. Some of this energy is transferred mechanically to the kinetic energy store of the ball *[1 mark]*. Some is transferred mechanically to the thermal energy stores of the golf club and the ball (and to the surroundings by heating) *[1 mark]*. The rest is carried away by sound *[1 mark]*.

Pages 52-53 — Sankey Diagrams

1 a) 10 J *[1 mark]*

You know the total input energy is 200 J. The input energy arrow is 20 squares wide, so the value of each square must be 200 J ÷ 20 = 10 J

   b) 50 J *[1 mark]*

The useful energy arrow is 5 squares wide, and each square represents 10 J. So the amount of energy that's usefully transferred = 5 × 10 J = 50 J

   c) E.g.

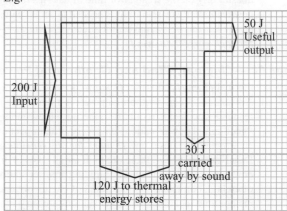

[1 mark for input width drawn correctly, 1 mark for all three output arrow widths drawn correctly, 1 mark for all arrows being correctly labelled.]

2 a) E.g. thermal energy store *[1 mark]*

   b) Energy transferred to weight = 100 – 50 – 20

= **30 kJ** *[1 mark]*

c) E.g.

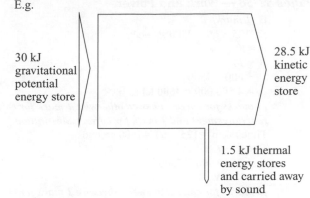

[1 mark for drawing a recognisable Sankey diagram, 1 mark for all of the arrows being drawn in roughly the correct proportions, 1 mark for all of the arrows being correctly labelled.]

Page 54 — Energy Transfer by Heating

1 a) Conduction *[1 mark]*
Radiation *[1 mark]*

   b) Flask C *[1 mark]*.
There is a larger temperature difference between flask C and the surrounding gel *[1 mark]*.

You receive no marks for this question if you answered A or B.

2   Conduction *[1 mark]*. As particles in the solid are heated, energy is transferred to their kinetic energy stores *[1 mark]*. The particles collide with neighbouring particles and transfer some of this energy to their kinetic energy stores, transferring the energy through the solid *[1 mark]*.

Page 55 — Convection

1 a) Solid *[1 mark]* because the particles are not free to move *[1 mark]*.

   b) i) E.g.

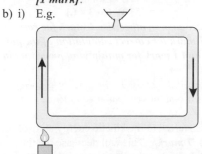

[1 mark for 2 arrows drawn anywhere inside the glass tube showing the correct flow of water]

   ii) The water particles near the heater gain energy (and get further apart) *[1 mark]*. This causes the water near the heater to expand and become less dense, so it rises up the pipe *[1 mark]*. Colder, denser water elsewhere in the pipe is displaced and moves to replace this heated water *[1 mark]*.

   c) C *[1 mark]*.

Page 56 — More Energy Transfers by Heating

1 a) Matt black *[1 mark]*

   b) Shiny white *[1 mark]*

   c) E.g. use an infrared detector to measure the emitted radiation / use a ruler to make sure he measures the radiation emitted from each side from the same distance *[1 mark for any sensible suggestion]*

2   Paper, cardboard and air have low thermal conductivity, so energy will be transferred through them by conduction quite slowly *[1 mark]*, which decreases the rate of energy transfer from the cup *[1 mark]*. The pockets of trapped air help prevent convection currents from forming around the outside of the cup *[1 mark]*.

Pages 57-58 — Work and Power

1   B *[1 mark]*

2 a) $t = 125 \times 60 = 7500$ seconds

       $P = W \div t$ so

       $W = Pt$

         $= 600 \times 7500$

         $= 4\,500\,000 = \textbf{4500 kJ}$

       [3 marks for correct answer, otherwise 1 mark for correct rearrangement and 1 mark for correct substitution.]

   b)   Time taken $= 125 \times 60 = 7500$ seconds

       $P = W \div t$

         $= 3\,930\,000 \div 7500$

         $= \textbf{524 W}$

       [2 marks for correct answer, otherwise 1 mark for correct substitution.]

3 a) i)   Work done = force applied × distance moved in the direction of the force / $W = Fd$ *[1 mark]*

     ii) $W = Fd$

          $= 50 \times 15$

          $= \textbf{750 J}$

        [2 marks for correct answer, otherwise 1 mark for correct substitution.]

   b)   The temperature of the wheel increases *[1 mark]* because doing work causes some energy to be transferred to the thermal energy store of the wheel *[1 mark]*.

4 a) $P = W \div t$

       Convert from kJ to J and from hours to seconds:

       $1.87 \times 10^3 \times 1000 = 1.87 \times 10^6$ J

       $1 \times 60 \times 60 = 3600$ s

       Power of old engine, $P_{old} = 1.87 \times 10^6 \div 3600$

                           $= 519.44...$ W

       New engine is 45% more powerful, so multiply old power by 1.45.

       Power of new engine, $P_{new} = 519.44 \times 1.45$

                             $= 753.1944...$ W

                             $= \textbf{753 W (to 3 s.f.)}$

       [4 marks for correct answer, otherwise 1 mark for correct unit conversion, 1 mark for correct calculation of the power of the old engine and 1 mark for multiplying power of old engine by 1.45.]

You could also have applied the 45% increase to the amount of energy transferred, and then substituted that into the power equation to find the power of the new engine.

   b)   More energy is transferred to the kinetic energy store of the moped per second *[1 mark]*. This will decrease the time *[1 mark]* needed to transfer enough energy to the moped's kinetic energy store to cause it to travel at 13 m/s *[1 mark]*.

Pages 59-60 — Kinetic and Potential Energy Stores

1   B *[1 mark]*

2 a)   energy in gravitational potential energy store = mass × gravitational field strength × height / $GPE = m \times g \times h$ *[1 mark]*

   b) $GPE = m \times g \times h$

            $= 65 \times 10 \times 10$

            $= \textbf{6500 J}$

       [2 marks for correct answer, otherwise 1 mark for correct substitution]

3 a)   4.0 J *[1 mark]*

When no air resistance acts, as an object falls, all the energy in its gravitational potential energy store is transferred to its kinetic energy store.

   b)   energy in kinetic energy store = ½ × mass × speed² / $KE = \frac{1}{2} \times m \times v^2$ *[1 mark]*

   c) $KE = \frac{1}{2} \times m \times v^2$

       Rearrange for mass:

       $m = 2 \times KE \div v^2$

         $= (2 \times 4.0) \div 8.9^2$

         $= 0.10099...$ kg

         $= \textbf{0.10 kg (to 2 s.f.)}$

       [3 marks for correct answer, otherwise 1 mark for correct rearrangement and 1 mark for correct substitution.]

4 a) $KE = \frac{1}{2} \times m \times v^2$

       $KE = \frac{1}{2} \times 105 \times 2.39^2$

           $= 299.8852...$ J

           $= \textbf{300 J (to 3 s.f.)}$

       [2 marks for correct answer, otherwise 1 mark for correct substitution.]

   b) i) $GPE = m \times g \times h$, so:

       energy lost from g.p.e. store $= 105 \times 10 \times 20.2$

                            $= 21\,210$ J

                            $= \textbf{21\,200 J (to 3 s.f.)}$

       [2 marks for correct answer, otherwise 1 mark for correct substitution.]

     ii)   It is transferred to the cart's kinetic energy store *[1 mark]*.

   c)   Energy lost from the g.p.e. store is transferred to the kinetic energy store,

       so $KE = 299.88... + 21\,210 = 21\,509.88...$ J

       $KE = \frac{1}{2} \times m \times v^2$

       Rearrange for speed:

       $v = \sqrt{\dfrac{2 \times KE}{m}}$

         $= \sqrt{\dfrac{2 \times 21509.88}{105}}$

         $= 20.2413...$ m/s

         $= \textbf{20.2 m/s (to 3 s.f.)}$

       [4 marks for correct answer, otherwise 1 mark for correct calculation of total energy in the kinetic energy store, 1 mark for correct rearrangement and 1 mark for correct substitution.]

Page 61 — Non-Renewable Energy and Power Stations

1   C *[1 mark]*

2   D *[1 mark]*

3 a)   As it is burnt, energy is transferred by heating from the chemical energy store of the natural gas to the thermal energy store of water, to turn the water into steam *[1 mark]*. The steam is used to drive turbines — transferring energy mechanically from the thermal energy store of the steam to the kinetic energy store of the turbine *[1 mark]*. The turbine drives a generator, so energy is transferred mechanically from the kinetic energy store of the turbine to the kinetic energy store of the generator *[1 mark]*. Energy is transferred away electrically to the national grid *[1 mark]*.

   b)   Any two from: e.g. burning natural gas releases a lot of energy for a relatively low cost / energy from natural gas doesn't rely on the weather or time of day (it's reliable) / no new technology or spending is needed to set up natural gas power stations — we have a lot already. *[2 marks — 1 mark for each correct answer.]*

Page 62 — Nuclear, Wind and Geothermal Power

1 a) i)   thermal *[1 mark]*, thermal *[1 mark]*, kinetic *[1 mark]*

     ii)   Advantage — e.g. geothermal power is a renewable resource / no fuel is required so there are low running costs / geothermal power stations have very little impact on the environment once set up. *[1 mark for any sensible answer.]*

       Disadvantage — e.g. there are high initial costs in drilling down several km / the cost of building a power station is often high compared to the amount of energy obtained / the possible locations for power stations are very limited. *[1 mark for any sensible answer.]*

   b)   Advantage — e.g. wind farms have low running costs (as there are no fuel costs) / wind is a renewable resource (it won't run out) / wind farms cause no atmospheric pollution. *[1 mark for any sensible answer.]*

       Disadvantage — e.g. some people think wind farms spoil the view/make too much noise / a lot of wind farms are needed to generate the same amount of electricity as a fossil fuel power station / wind speed varies, so they're not particularly reliable / wind farms usually require specific (remote) locations, so building and maintenance work is expensive / you can't increase the supply of electricity when demand is high. *[1 mark for any sensible answer.]*

2 a) Energy is transferred by heating from the nuclear energy store of the fuel to the thermal energy store of the water/steam *[1 mark]*.

b) i) Nuclear fuels don't release any greenhouse gases (e.g. carbon dioxide) that contribute to global warming *[1 mark]*.

ii) Any two from: e.g. processing or transporting the nuclear fuel before it is used causes atmospheric pollution / nuclear power stations carry the risk of major catastrophes (like Chernobyl), which have a huge impact on the environment / radioactive waste is difficult to dispose of and is harmful to the environment/humans. *[2 marks — 1 mark for each correct answer.]*

Page 63 — Solar and Wave Power

1 a) D *[1 mark]*

b) Energy is transferred mechanically from the kinetic energy store of the waves to the kinetic energy stores of the turbine and generator *[1 mark]*.

2 a) A solar cell *[1 mark]*

b) E.g. solar water heating panels *[1 mark]* — they absorb energy from the Sun to heat water inside them. This hot water can then be supplied to the home *[1 mark]*.

c) E.g. the cost of connecting solar cells to the national grid is high compared to the amount of electricity they generate *[1 mark]*. It is often not practical to connect them to the national grid *[1 mark]*.

Page 64 — Generating Electricity Using Water

1 a) Energy is transferred from the gravitational potential energy store of the water to the kinetic energy store of the water, then to the kinetic energy stores of the turbines and the generator *[1 mark]*. Electricity is generated and the energy is transferred electrically from the generator to the national grid *[1 mark]*.

b) Any two from: e.g. they can cause the loss or destruction of habitats / rotting vegetation in flooded areas releases methane/CO_2/greenhouse gases / they can change the landscape drastically. *[2 marks — 1 mark for each correct answer.]*

c) Pumped storage *[1 mark]*.

d) Any two from: e.g. they cause no atmospheric pollution / they use a renewable energy source / there are no fuel costs / maintenance and running costs are low / tides are regular and predictable, so this is a fairly reliable energy source. *[2 marks — 1 mark for each correct answer.]*

Section 5 — Solids, Liquids and Gases

Pages 65-66 — Density and Pressure

1 C *[1 mark]*.

2 a) The volume of the pendant *[1 mark]*.
The mass of the pendant *[1 mark]*.

b) E.g. measure the mass of the pendant using the mass balance *[1 mark]*. Fill the eureka can with water to just below the spout, then place the measuring cylinder beneath the spout *[1 mark]*. To measure the volume of the pendant, submerge the pendant in the water, catching the displaced water in the measuring cylinder *[1 mark]*. Measure the volume of the displaced water, which is equal to the volume of the pendant *[1 mark]*. Divide the mass of the pendant by the volume of the pendant to find the density *[1 mark]*.

With questions where you have to describe a method, make sure your description is clear and detailed. You could also pick up some of the marks by describing how you'd do repeats, take averages and other ways in which you'd make it a fair test.

3 a) The pressure increases with depth *[1 mark]*.

b) i) pressure = $\dfrac{\text{force}}{\text{area}}$ / $p = \dfrac{F}{A}$ *[1 mark]*

ii) 4500 cm^2 = 0.45 m^2
$p = \dfrac{F}{A} = \dfrac{18}{0.45} = $ **40 Pa**
[3 marks if answer correct, otherwise 1 mark for converting area to m^2 and 1 mark for correct substitution of values into the equation.]

4 a) pressure difference
= height × density × gravitational field strength /
$p = h \times \rho \times g$
[1 mark]

b) i) $\rho = \dfrac{m}{V} = \dfrac{514}{0.500}$
$= 1028 = $ **1030 kg/m^3 (to 3 s.f.)**
[2 marks if answer correct, otherwise 1 mark for correct substitution.]

ii) 245 kPa = 245 × 10^3 = 245 000 Pa
$p = h \times \rho \times g \Rightarrow h = \dfrac{p}{\rho \times g} = \dfrac{245\,000}{1028 \times 10} = 23.83...$
$= $ **24 m (to 2 s.f.)**
[3 marks if answer correct, otherwise 1 mark for correct rearrangement of the equation and 1 mark for correct substitution of values into the equation.]

You'll still get the marks if the density you used from part b) i) was incorrect.

Page 67 — Changes of State

1 a) i) Particles are held close together in a fixed, regular pattern *[1 mark]*. They vibrate about fixed positions *[1 mark]*.

ii) gas(es) *[1 mark]*

b) i) melting *[1 mark]*

ii) When the substance is changing state, the energy provided when it is heated is used to break intermolecular bonds *[1 mark]* rather than raise the temperature, so the substance stays at a constant temperature *[1 mark]*.

c) i) Evaporation *[1 mark]*. A liquid can evaporate at temperatures that are lower than the liquid's boiling point, whereas boiling happens only at the boiling point *[1 mark]*. Particles in the liquid can only evaporate if they are travelling in the right direction, fast enough to overcome the attractive forces of the other particles in the liquid, whereas when a liquid boils, all of the particles have enough energy to escape *[1 mark]*.

ii) When a liquid evaporates the fastest particles are most likely to escape the liquid *[1 mark]*. When they do, the average speed/energy in the kinetic energy stores of the remaining particles in the liquid decreases *[1 mark]*. The drop in average speed/energy causes a drop in temperature *[1 mark]*.

Page 68 — Temperature and Particle Theory

1 a) i) The average speed decreases *[1 mark]*.

ii) The energy of the particles in a substance decreases with temperature *[1 mark]*. There is a minimum energy that the particles can have, so there is a minimum temperature *[1 mark]*.

iii) –273 °C *[1 mark]*

b)

Temperature (K)	Temperature (°C)
10	–263
904	631

[2 marks available — 1 mark for each correct temperature.]
To convert from the Kelvin scale to the Celsius scale just subtract 273, and to convert from the Celsius scale to the Kelvin scale add 273.

2 a) The substance is melting *[1 mark]*.

b) Melting point = –7 °C *[1 mark]*
Boiling point = 58 °C *[1 mark]*

Page 69 — Particle Theory and Pressure in Gases

1    $\frac{p_1}{T_1} = \frac{p_2}{T_2} \Rightarrow p_2 = \frac{p_1 \times T_2}{T_1} = \frac{107 \times 405}{288} = 150.4...$
$$= \textbf{150 kPa (to 3 s.f.)}$$
[3 marks if answer correct, otherwise 1 mark for correct rearrangement of the equation and 1 mark for correct substitution of values into the equation.]

2 a) i) The pressure increases *[1 mark]*. This is because the volume decrease leads to the number of collisions in a given time on a given area between particles and the walls of the cylinder increasing *[1 mark]* and so the force applied by the particles to the cylinder walls increases *[1 mark]*.

   ii) $p_1V_1 = p_2V_2 \Rightarrow p_2 = \frac{p_1V_1}{V_2} = \frac{98 \times 0.014}{0.013}$
$$= 105.53... = \textbf{110 kPa (to 2 s.f.)}$$
[3 marks if answer correct, otherwise 1 mark for correct rearrangement of the equation and 1 mark for correct substitution of values into the equation.]

   b) As the gas is heated, the average energy in the kinetic energy stores of the particles increases *[1 mark]*. This means they move faster and collide with the walls more often in a given time *[1 mark]*, increasing the outwards force/pressure on the walls of the cylinder *[1 mark]*.

Page 70 — Specific Heat Capacity

1   D *[1 mark]*.

2 a) E.g. measure the mass of the empty insulated flask and then fill it with the liquid you are testing. Measure the mass of the flask again to find the mass of the liquid *[1 mark]*. Connect the power supply to the joulemeter and the immersion heater. Place the immersion heater into the liquid *[1 mark]*. Measure the temperature of the liquid *[1 mark]* and then turn on the immersion heater. Turn off the immersion heater once the temperature of the liquid has increased by 10 °C *[1 mark]*. Read the energy transferred shown on the joulemeter and use $\Delta Q = mc\Delta T$ to calculate the specific heat capacity *[1 mark]*.

   b) $\Delta Q = mc\Delta T$ so $c = \Delta Q \div m\Delta T$
$$= 15\,000 \div (0.3 \times 25)$$
$c = \textbf{2000 J/kg °C}$
[3 marks for correct answer, otherwise 1 mark for rearranging, 1 mark for correct substitution.]

Section 6 — Magnetism and Electromagnetism

Page 71 — Magnets and Magnetic Fields

1 a) The field is uniform / The field lines are straight, parallel and evenly spaced *[1 mark]*.

   b) Attraction *[1 mark]* — opposite poles attract *[1 mark]*.

2 a) E.g. put the magnets on a piece of paper and place many compasses in different places between the magnets to show the magnetic field at those points *[1 mark]*. The compasses will line up with the magnetic field lines *[1 mark]*.
You could also use iron filings to shown the pattern.

   b) E.g.

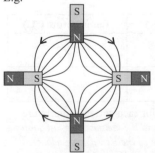

[2 marks for four correct arrows, otherwise 1 mark for two correct arrows, each one placed between a different pair of magnets. Do not award any marks for contradicting arrows.]

   c) A material that becomes magnetised when placed in a magnetic field *[1 mark]*.

   d) The north pole of the bar magnet induces a south/opposite pole in the head of the nail *[1 mark]* and the opposite poles attract each other *[1 mark]*.

Pages 72-73 — Electromagnetism

1 a) A *[1 mark]*.

   b)

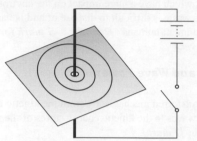

[1 mark for drawing concentric circles centred around the copper rod.]

   c)

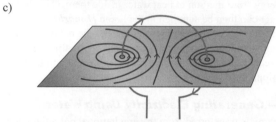

[1 mark for correct pattern, 1 mark for arrows shown in correct directions.]

2 a) A coil of wire *[1 mark]*.

   b)

coil of wire   magnetic field

Inside the coil, the field is strong and uniform. Outside the coil, the field is the same as that of a bar magnet.
[1 mark for showing by sketch or for saying that the field is uniform and strong inside the coil and 1 mark for showing by sketch or saying that the field is like that of a bar magnet outside the coil.]

   c) When the electromagnet is turned on, current flows through the coil of wire and produces a magnetic field *[1 mark]*. Iron is a magnetic material, so magnetism is induced in it and the bar is attracted to the electromagnet *[1 mark]*. When the current stops, there is no longer a magnetic field around the electromagnet *[1 mark]* so magnetism is no longer induced and the bar is no longer attracted to the electromagnet and drops *[1 mark]*.

   d) i) A magnetic material that loses its induced magnetism quickly *[1 mark]*.

     ii) Magnetically hard materials don't lose their magnetism quickly *[1 mark]*, so when the electromagnet is turned off the core will stay magnetic for a while and still attract the iron bar, meaning the crane won't drop the iron bar *[1 mark]*.

Page 74 — The Motor Effect

1 a) i) A current-carrying wire in a magnetic field experiences a force *[1 mark]*.

     ii) out of the page (towards you/the reader) *[1 mark]*

   b) i) The force will increase *[1 mark]*.

     ii) Reversing the direction of the magnetic field *[1 mark]*. Reversing the direction of the current *[1 mark]*.

2   The electrons that form the current through the bar are moving parallel to the magnetic field *[1 mark]* so they (and the bar) will experience no force *[1 mark]*.

Page 75 — Electric Motors and Loudspeakers

1 a)   E.g.

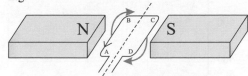

    [1 mark for any indication that the current goes anticlockwise.]

   b)   After 90° the force on the coil between A and B will act upwards and the force on the coil between C and D will act downwards, so the forces will oppose the rotation of the loop *[1 mark]*.

   c)   By swapping the direction of the current/contacts every half turn (using a split-ring commutator) *[1 mark]* so the forces on the loop always act in a way that keeps the loop rotating *[1 mark]*.

   d)   Any one of: e.g. increase the current / increase the number of turns on the loop / increase the strength of the magnetic field / add a soft iron coil to the coil *[1 mark]*.

2   When the alternating current flows through the coil of wire in the magnetic field of the permanent magnet, the coil of wire experiences a force *[1 mark]*. The force causes the coil, and so the cone, to move *[1 mark]*. The alternating current is constantly changing direction so the force on the coil is constantly changing, so the cone vibrates back and forth *[1 mark]*. The vibrations cause the air to vibrate and cause sound waves *[1 mark]*.

Pages 76-77: Electromagnetic Induction

1   C *[1 mark]*

2 a)   As the wheel rotates, the magnet rotates inside the coil of wire *[1 mark]*. This creates a changing magnetic field in the coil of wire which induces a voltage *[1 mark]*.

   b)   Any two of: e.g. increase the strength of the magnet / increase the number of turns on the coil of wire / increase the speed of rotation of the magnet *[2 marks — 1 mark for each correct answer]*.

   c)   It does not matter. There will be a changing magnetic field through the wire when the magnet rotates in either direction *[1 mark]*.

3 a)   Rotating the handle causes the coil to rotate (move) within the magnetic field, which creates a changing magnetic field and so a voltage and current are induced in the circuit *[1 mark]*. The direction of the wire's movement in relation to the magnetic field changes every half turn and so the direction of the current induced changes (an alternating current) *[1 mark]*.

   b) E.g.

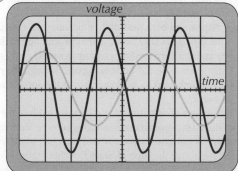

    [2 marks available — 1 mark for drawing a trace with a larger voltage than the original trace and 1 mark for drawing a trace with a higher frequency than the original trace.]

   c)   The trace would be the same *[1 mark]*.

Pages 78-79 — Transformers

1   B *[1 mark]*

2 a)   Step-down, because the voltage decreases (from 240 V to 12 V) *[1 mark]*.

   b) i)   Power = current × voltage / $P = I \times V$ *[1 mark]*

     ii)   If the transformer is 100 % efficient, input power = output power. $P = VI$, so $V_p I_p = V_s I_s$

      So current in secondary coil, $I_s = \dfrac{V_p I_p}{V_s}$

$$I_s = \frac{240 \times 0.25}{12} = \textbf{5 A}$$

      [4 marks for correct answer, otherwise 1 mark for stating input power = output power, 1 mark for correct rearrangement and 1 mark for correct substitution.]

3 a)   A step-up transformer is used to increase the voltage of electricity transmitted from power stations to a very high level *[1 mark]*. A higher voltage means less current for a given power ($P = I \times V$) and so less energy is lost by heating *[1 mark]*. Step-down transformers are then used to bring the voltage of the supply back down to a safe level to be supplied to the consumer *[1 mark]*.

   b) i) $\dfrac{\text{input (primary) voltage}}{\text{output (secondary) voltage}} = \dfrac{\text{number of turns on primary}}{\text{number of turns on secondary}}$

$$\left(\frac{V_p}{V_s} = \frac{N_p}{N_s} \right) \text{ [1 mark]}$$

     ii)   There are 16 times more coils on the secondary coil than on the primary coil, so

$$\frac{N_s}{N_p} = 16$$

$$\frac{V_p}{V_s} = \frac{N_p}{N_s} \text{ so } V_s = \frac{N_s}{N_p} \times V_p = 16 \times 25\,000 = \textbf{400\,000 V}$$

      [3 marks for correct answer, otherwise 1 mark for rearranging the equation correctly and 1 mark for substituting correctly into the equation.]

   c)   If the current was direct, its direction wouldn't change so the magnetic field created by the primary coil wouldn't change *[1 mark]*. This means the magnetic field through the secondary coil wouldn't change *[1 mark]*, so no voltage would be induced across it *[1 mark]*.

Section 7 — Radioactivity and Particles

Page 80 — Radioactivity

1 a) i)

Particle	Charge	Number present in an atom of iodine-131
Proton	positive	53
Neutron	zero	78
Electron	negative	53

     [3 marks — 1 mark for each correct answer]

     ii)   protons and neutrons *[1 mark]*

   b)   A *[1 mark]*

Isotopes have the same number of protons but a different number of neutrons, so they have the same atomic number (no. of protons) but a different mass number (no. of protons and neutrons). The number of protons always equals the number of electrons in a neutral atom (i.e. not an ion).

   c) i)   background radiation *[1 mark]*

     ii)   Any two from: e.g. air / food / building materials / soils / rocks / radiation from space (cosmic rays) / living things *[2 marks — 1 mark for each correct answer]*.

   d)   gamma (rays) *[1 mark]*, alpha (particles) *[1 mark]*, beta (particles) *[1 mark]*, neutrons *[1 mark]*

Page 81 — Ionising Radiation

1 a) i) The atom loses an electron, causing the atom to have an overall positive charge (becoming an ion) *[1 mark]*.
   ii) Alpha (particles) *[1 mark]* because they are large and heavy, so they collide with lots of atoms, causing ionisation *[1 mark]*.
  b) i) gamma (rays) *[1 mark]*
   ii) beta (particles) *[1 mark]*
2 a) The atomic number doesn't change *[1 mark]* and neither does the mass number *[1 mark]*.
  b) 208 *[1 mark]*. Alpha decay reduces the mass number by 4 as 2 neutrons and 2 protons are emitted as an alpha particle *[1 mark]*. Beta decay doesn't affect the mass number as a neutron turns into a proton in the nucleus. Gamma decay doesn't affect the mass number (or the atomic number). So the overall effect is the mass number decreasing by 4 *[1 mark]*.

Page 82 — Investigating Radiation and Nuclear Equations

1 a) Beta (particles) *[1 mark]*, because it passes through the paper, but not the aluminium (so it is moderately penetrating) *[1 mark]*.
  b) photographic film *[1 mark]*
  c) Background radiation is not due to the sources the student is using in the experiment *[1 mark]*. The student needs to subtract the background count rate so that her results only include the radiation emitted by the source *[1 mark]*.
2 a) $^{1}_{0}n$ *[1 mark]*
  b) $^{199}_{84}Po \rightarrow ^{195}_{82}Pb + ^{4}_{2}\alpha + ^{0}_{0}\gamma$

   [4 marks — 1 mark for the α atomic and mass numbers correct, 1 mark for the γ atomic and mass numbers correct, and 1 mark each for the mass and atomic numbers of Po.]

Pages 83-84 — Half-Life

1 a) becquerels / Bq *[1 mark]*
  b) The half-life is the time taken for half of the unstable atoms present to decay *[1 mark]*.
You'd also get the marks for saying it is the time taken for the activity (or count rate) to fall by half.
2 a) i) $2 \times 60 = 120$ seconds
   $120 \div 40 = 3$ half-lives
   $8000 \div 2 = 4000$, $4000 \div 2 = 2000$, $2000 \div 2 =$ **1000 Bq**
   [2 marks for the correct answer, otherwise 1 mark for calculating the number of half-lives.]
   ii) $8000 \div 2 = 4000$, $4000 \div 2 = 2000$, $2000 \div 2 = 1000$, $1000 \div 2 = 500$, $500 \div 2 = 250$, $250 \div 2 = 125$. So it takes 6 half-lives to drop to less than 200 Bq.
   $6 \times 40 = 240$ seconds
   $240 \div 60 =$ **4 mins**
   [3 marks for the correct answer, otherwise 1 mark for calculating the number of half-lives and 1 mark for calculating the number of seconds.]
  b) A *[1 mark]*
3 a) E.g. to get a measure of the background radiation *[1 mark]* so that the processed results can take it into account *[1 mark]*.

b)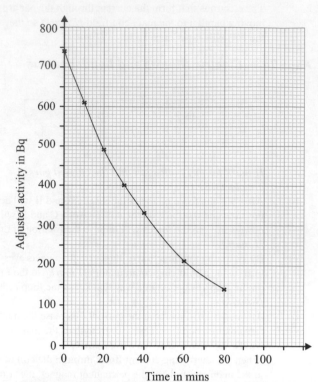

   [1 mark for suitable scales chosen (at least half the graph paper used), 1 mark for a curve of best fit, 1 mark for axes labelled (with variables and units), 1 mark for correctly plotted points. Deduct up to 2 marks for incorrectly plotted points, 1 mark per incorrect point.]
  c) 34 minutes
   [1 mark — accept answer in range 32-36 minutes]
  d) The older sample would have a lower count rate/activity (in Bq) *[1 mark]* because more of its nuclei will have already decayed so it will emit less radiation *[1 mark]*.
The samples are identical so they'll have the same half-life.

Pages 85-86 — Uses of Nuclear Radiation

1 D *[1 mark]*
2 a) Iodine-123 is injected into/ingested by the patient, where it gives out radiation which can be detected outside the body *[1 mark]*. The amount of radiation emitted from the thyroid gland is monitored to check whether it is absorbing iodine properly *[1 mark]*.
  b) Alpha particles can't penetrate tissue/are blocked by the body *[1 mark]*, so you can't detect them outside of the body *[1 mark]*. Alpha particles are also strongly ionising *[1 mark]* so they're dangerous to use as medical tracers *[1 mark]*.
  c) Technetium-99m because it's got a short half-life *[1 mark]*, which means it's easier to detect because its activity is higher/ won't be very radioactive inside the patient for long *[1 mark]*.
3 a) i) Gamma *[1 mark]*
   ii) Either: Alpha and beta wouldn't be detected on the surface above the pipe *[1 mark]* because they would be blocked by the pipe and the surrounding ground *[1 mark]*.
   Or: Only gamma would be able to pass through the pipe and ground *[1 mark]* and so be detectable at the surface above the pipe *[1 mark]*.
  b) E.g. the source of radiation could be injected into the pipeline before the first point where it is thought to be leaking *[1 mark]*. A radiation sensor would then be passed along the surface above the pipe *[1 mark]*. Where there is a leak, the source will escape from the pipe and there will be a high reading above that part of the pipe *[1 mark]*.

4   After one half-life, the number of carbon-14 atoms will have halved, so the ratio will go from $1:10^{12}$ to $1:(2 \times 10^{12})$.
After two half-lives it will be $1:(4 \times 10^{12})$.
After three half-lives it will be $1:(8 \times 10^{12})$.
So the wood was alive 3 half-lives ago
$3 \times 5730 = \textbf{17 190 years}$.
[3 marks for correct answer, otherwise 1 mark for correctly stating 3 half-lives and 1 mark for attempting to multiply the half-life by 3.]

Page 87 — Risks from Nuclear Radiation

1 a)   E.g. when radiation enters the body, it can collide with molecules in body cells causing ionisation *[1 mark]* which can damage or destroy the molecules / cause cell damage/cell death/cancer/radiation sickness *[1 mark]*.

  b)   E.g. some radioactive waste has a very high activity *[1 mark]* so needs to be heavily shielded *[1 mark]*. / Radioactive waste has a very long half-life (hundreds of thousands of years) *[1 mark]*, so needs to be safely out of reach of generations to come *[1 mark]*.

2 a)   Contamination is when unwanted radioactive particles get onto an object *[1 mark]*.

  b)   Irradiation: Any one of: e.g. use shielding/stand behind barriers / work in a different room to the source / store the sample in a lead-lined box *[1 mark]*.
Contamination: Any one of: e.g. wear gloves / handle the source with tongs / wear a protective suit or mask *[1 mark]*.

3   E.g. He should be more concerned about contamination *[1 mark]*. Although alpha particles are highly ionising *[1 mark]* and can do damage to skin, they can't penetrate into the body and damage tissues or organs *[1 mark]*. Contamination by an alpha source (e.g. ingesting / breathing it in) could lead to alpha particles inside the body, where they can do lots of damage to nearby tissues or organs *[1 mark]*.

Page 88 — Nuclear Fission

1 a)   E.g. uranium-235/U-235 *[1 mark]*

  b) i)   A slow-moving neutron gets absorbed by a uranium-235 nucleus causing it to split *[1 mark]*. The uranium nucleus will split to form two daughter nuclei *[1 mark]* and a small number of neutrons *[1 mark]*. The fission products have a large amount of energy in their kinetic energy stores *[1 mark]*.

    ii)   In a nuclear reactor, the neutrons released from each fission event can collide with other uranium nuclei causing other fission events that release more neutrons *[1 mark]*. This is known as a chain reaction *[1 mark]*. The nuclear reactor contains a moderator that slows down the neutrons released from fission so that they can successfully collide with uranium nuclei *[1 mark]*.

  c)   They limit the rate of fission by absorbing excess neutrons *[1 mark]*.

Page 89 — Nuclear Fusion

1   B *[1 mark]*

2 a)   Nuclear fusion is when two light nuclei join/fuse together to create a larger nucleus *[1 mark]*.

  b)   B *[1 mark]*

The energy released from nuclear fusion is due to a difference in the mass of the nuclei before (greater) and after (smaller).

3   A high temperature and pressure is needed for the reaction to take place *[1 mark]*. This is because the protons are positive, so they repel each other *[1 mark]*. To get close enough to fuse together, they need to overcome this electrostatic repulsion. This means they need lots of energy in their kinetic energy stores *[1 mark]*.

Section 8 — Astrophysics

Page 90 — The Universe

1   B *[1 mark]*

2 a)   The Milky Way *[1 mark]*

  b)   circular *[1 mark]*

  c)

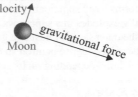

[1 mark for arrow pointed from centre of Moon towards centre of Earth, 1 mark for arrow correctly labelled as gravitational force/gravity]

Pages 91-92 — Gravity and Orbits

1   C *[1 mark]*

2 a)   C *[1 mark]* — Comets usually have highly elliptical orbits with the Sun not at the centre *[1 mark]*.

  b)   1.2 km/s — orbital speed only depends on the orbital radius and the time period. *[1 mark]*

  c)   Convert time period to s, $T = 24 \times 60 \times 60 = 86400$ s
Convert radius to m, $r = 24\,000 \times 1000 = 24\,000\,000$ m
$$v = \frac{2 \times \pi \times r}{T}$$
$$= \frac{2 \times \pi \times 42\,000\,000}{86400}$$
$$= 3054.326...$$
$$= \textbf{3100 m/s}$$
[3 marks if answer correct, otherwise 1 mark for correct conversion of units and 1 mark for correct substitution of values into the equation.]

3 a)   time period $= 72 \times 365 \times 24 \times 60 \times 60$
$$= 2\,270\,592\,000 \text{ s}$$
$$= \textbf{2.27} \times \textbf{10}^9 \textbf{ s (to 3 s.f.)} \text{ } \textit{[1 mark]}$$

There are 365 days in a year, 24 hours in a day, 60 minutes in an hour and 60 seconds in a minute — that's where all these numbers come from.

  b)   At the point where the comet is at its closest point to the star *[1 mark]* because that's where the gravitational force on the comet from the star is strongest *[1 mark]*.

  c)   Convert km/s to m/s,
$v = 7.4 \times 1000 = 7400$ m/s
$$v = \frac{2 \times \pi \times r}{T}$$
Rearrange for orbital radius,
$$r = \frac{v \times T}{2 \times \pi}$$
$$= \frac{7400 \times 2\,270\,592\,000}{2 \times \pi}$$
$$= 2.6741... \times 10^{12} \text{ m}$$
$$= \textbf{2.67} \times \textbf{10}^{12} \textbf{ m (to 3 s.f.)}$$
[3 marks if answer correct, otherwise 1 mark for correct rearrangement of the equation and 1 mark for correct substitution of values into the equation.]

Page 93 — Stellar Evolution

1 a)   B *[1 mark]*

  b)   A cloud of dust and gas *[1 mark]*

  c)   gravitational force / gravity *[1 mark]*

2   The star initially forms from a nebula (a cloud of dust and gas) that is drawn together by the force of gravity (to form a protostar) *[1 mark]*. As the dust and gas are drawn together, the star gets denser and hotter (and the particles of dust and gas collide more). Eventually, the temperature gets hot enough for hydrogen nuclei to undergo nuclear fusion to form helium, and the star becomes a main sequence star *[1 mark]*. When the star runs out of hydrogen, it expands and turns red and forms a red supergiant *[1 mark]*. The red supergiant eventually explodes in a supernova *[1 mark]*. The supernova throws the outer layer of dust and gas into space, leaving behind either a very dense neutron star *[1 mark]*, or an even denser black hole, depending on its size *[1 mark]*.

Page 94 — Classifying Stars

1 a)   D *[1 mark]*

  b)   Alkaid is the brightest star *[1 mark]* as it has the lowest absolute magnitude (and the lower the absolute magnitude the brighter the star) *[1 mark]*.

2 a)   absolute magnitude *[1 mark]*

  b)

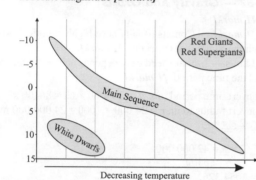

[1 mark for a group drawn in the bottom left, 1 mark for a group drawn diagonally from top-left to bottom right, 1 mark for a group drawn in the top-right, 1 mark for all groups labelled correctly]

Page 95 — Red-shift

1   There is an observed increase in the wavelength (or decrease in frequency) of the light from light sources that are moving away from the observer *[1 mark]*, so the light is shifted towards the red end of the electromagnetic spectrum *[1 mark]*.

2 a) $\Delta\lambda = 612.5 \times 10^{-9} - 587.5 \times 10^{-9} = 25 \times 10^{-9}$ m

$$\frac{\Delta\lambda}{\lambda_0} = \frac{v}{c}$$

Rearrange for velocity,

$$v = \frac{\Delta\lambda \times c}{\lambda_0} = \frac{(25 \times 10^{-9}) \times (3.0 \times 10^8)}{587.5 \times 10^{-9}}$$

$$= 1.27659... \times 10^7 \text{ m/s}$$

$$= \mathbf{1.3 \times 10^7 \text{ m/s (to 2 s.f.)}}$$

[3 marks for correct answer, otherwise 1 mark for correct calculation of $\Delta\lambda$ and 1 mark for correct rearrangement and substitution.]

  b) $\frac{\Delta\lambda}{\lambda_0} = \frac{v}{c}$

Rearrange for $\Delta\lambda$,

$$\Delta\lambda = \frac{v \times \lambda_0}{c} = \frac{(1.27659... \times 10^7) \times (686.7 \times 10^{-9})}{3.0 \times 10^8}$$

$$= 29.221... \times 10^{-9} \text{ m}$$

$$\lambda = \lambda_0 + \Delta\lambda = 686.7 \times 10^{-9} + 29.221... \times 10^{-9}$$

$$= 715.921... \times 10^{-9}$$

$$= \mathbf{715.9 \times 10^{-9} \text{ m } \textit{or } 7.159 \times 10^{-7} \text{ m (to 4 s.f.)}}$$

[3 marks for correct answer, otherwise 1 mark for correct rearrangement and substitution and 1 mark for correct calculation of $\Delta\lambda$.]

You'd still have gotten all the marks for part b) if you got the answer to part a) wrong, as long as your method in b) was correct.

Page 96 — The Big Bang

1 a)   Tadpole Galaxy *[1 mark]*. It is the furthest away *[1 mark]*, so it is travelling away fastest, so it would show the greatest red-shift *[1 mark]*.

  b) i)   Measurements of red-shift show all the distant galaxies, (whichever direction you look in) are moving away from us *[1 mark]*, and that the more distant a galaxy, the faster it's moving away *[1 mark]*. This suggests that the universe is expanding from a single point *[1 mark]*. Something must have initially started them moving, which we think was the Big Bang *[1 mark]*.

    ii)   E.g. the Cosmic Microwave Background radiation (CMB radiation) *[1 mark]*

Practice Paper 1P

1 a) i) B *[1 mark]*
   ii) B *[1 mark]*
   b) i) Gravitational potential energy = mass × gravitational field strength × height / GPE = $m × g × h$ *[1 mark]*
   ii) GPE = $m × g × h$ = 1500 × 10 × 40 = 600 000 J = **600 kJ**
   [2 marks for correct answer in kJ, otherwise 1 mark for substituting the correct values into the correct equation.]
   c) i) elastic potential energy store (of the spring) *[1 mark]*
   ii) efficiency = $\frac{\text{useful energy output}}{\text{total energy output}} × 100\%$ *[1 mark]*
   iii) useful energy output = 18.0 kJ
   total energy output = useful energy output + wasted energy
   = 18.0 + 41.5 = 59.5 kJ
   So efficiency = $\frac{\text{useful energy output}}{\text{total energy output}} × 100\% = \frac{18.0}{59.5} × 100\%$
   = **30.3% (to 3 s.f.)**
   [3 marks available for correct answer, otherwise 1 mark for calculating the total energy output (and input) and 1 mark for substituting correctly into correct equation.]

2 a) 27 s *[1 mark]*
   b) i) The gradient tells you the speed, so speed is constant when graph is linear. Graph is linear between 15 s and 27 s.
   27 – 15 = **12 s** *[1 mark]*
   ii) 0 N *[1 mark]*
   When an object is travelling at a constant speed in a fixed direction, all the forces are balanced and so the resultant force will be zero.
   c) B *[1 mark]*.
   The swimmer is travelling fastest when the gradient of the graph is steepest. Of the options given, the graph is steepest between 9 m and 10 m. You can draw a tangent to see this more clearly.
   d) i) (average) speed = $\frac{\text{distance moved}}{\text{time taken}}$ / $v = \frac{s}{t}$ *[1 mark]*
   ii) $v = \frac{s}{t} = \frac{20}{25}$ = **0.8 m/s**
   [2 marks for correct answer, otherwise 1 mark for correct substitution.]
   iii)

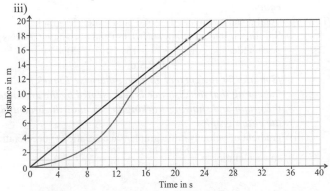

[1 mark for straight line, 1 mark for correct start and end points.]
   e) Yes, the camera will be able to film the swimmer for the whole length because its distance-time graph is always above the swimmer's *[1 mark]*, and so the camera is always ahead of the swimmer (or level at $t = 0$) *[1 mark]*.

3 a) The thickness of the cotton wool jacket *[1 mark]*.
   b) E.g. starting temperature of the water / length of time water is left to cool / volume of water used *[1 mark]*.
   c) The pockets of air cannot move *[1 mark]*, which prevents convection currents from forming around the outside of the beaker *[1 mark]*.
   d) i) Calculate the mean (average) of her data for each cotton wool jacket thickness *[1 mark]*.
   ii) E.g. the graph shows that for this beaker of water, the final temperature of the water increases with the thickness of the cotton wool jacket *[1 mark]*.

4 a) Stopping distance = thinking distance + braking distance
   = 9 + 14 = **23 m** *[1 mark]*
   b) E.g. so that an average value can be calculated *[1 mark]*. This makes the data more reliable because any individual vehicle may have an extreme value of braking distance / because any individual driver may have an extreme value of thinking distance *[1 mark]*.
   c) Any three from: e.g. The thinking distance is increased if the driver is: tired / under the influence of drugs/alcohol / elderly / inexperienced.
   The braking distance is increased: in poor weather conditions / if the surface of the road is slippery / if the car is heavier / if the brakes/tyres are worn/faulty.
   [5 marks available — 1 mark for each correct factor (up to 3 total) and 2 marks for all correctly linked to braking or thinking distance, otherwise 1 mark for only two correctly linked to braking or thinking distance.]

5 a) gravity *[1 mark]*
   b) $v = \frac{2 × \pi × r}{T}$ where r is the distance from the satellite to the centre of the Earth.
   Convert T to seconds, T = 24 × 60 × 60 = 86 400 s
   so $r = \frac{v × T}{2 × \pi} = \frac{3080 × 86 400}{2 × \pi}$
   = 42 353 040.2... m = **42 400 000 m (to 3 s.f.)**
   [3 marks for correct answer, otherwise 1 mark for converting the time period to seconds, 1 mark for correctly rearranging and substituting into the equation.]
   c) The object will weigh less on Venus than on Earth *[1 mark]* as the gravitational field strength on Venus is lower than on Earth (and weight is proportional to gravitational field strength) *[1 mark]*.
   d) red giant (star) *[1 mark]*

6 a) Any two from: e.g. it can cause cell/tissue damage *[1 mark]* / cell death *[1 mark]* / cell mutations/cancer *[1 mark]* / radiation sickness *[1 mark]*.
   b) Geiger-Müller detector *[1 mark]*
   c) i)

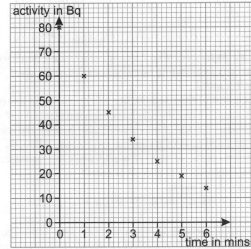

[3 marks available — 1 mark for suitable scales chosen (more than half of the graph paper is used), 1 mark for the axes correctly labelled with variables and units, 1 mark for all the points plotted correctly to within half a square. Deduct 1 mark if 2 or more points are plotted incorrectly.]

ii)

[1 mark for curve of best fit starting at point (0, 80), 1 mark for suitable curve of best fit.]

iii) Half-life = **2.4 mins** *(accept any value between 2.3-2.5)*
Draw a horizontal line from 40 Bq (half of the initial activity) on the activity axis across to the curve. Then draw a vertical line down to the time axis to find the value of the half-life.

[2 marks for correct answer, otherwise 1 mark for attempting to use the graph correctly to find the half-life.]

d) Any one from: e.g. some substances on Earth, such as air/food/building materials/soil/rocks *[1 mark]*. / Radiation from space/cosmic rays *[1 mark]*. / All living things contain radioactive material *[1 mark]*. / Nuclear waste *[1 mark]*. / Radioactive material released from past nuclear explosions *[1 mark]*.

e) i) $^{226}_{88}Ra \rightarrow {}^{222}_{86}Rn + {}^{4}_{2}\alpha$ *[1 mark]*

ii) C *[1 mark]*

7 a) current *[1 mark]*

b) i) E.g. he has not ignored the anomalous point *[1 mark]*.

ii) Voltage = current × resistance / $V = I \times R$ *[1 mark]*

iii) $V = 5\,V$, $I = 1.4\,A$

$V = I \times R$ so $R = \dfrac{V}{I} = \dfrac{5}{1.4} = $ **3.6 ohms (Ω) (to 2 s.f.)**

[3 marks for the correct answer, otherwise 1 mark for correctly substituting into the equation and 1 mark for the correct unit.]

c) i) The graph of the fixed resistor will be a straight line (through the origin), while the graph for the lamp is a curve *[1 mark]*.

ii) The shapes of the graphs are different because the resistance of the fixed resistor is constant (so current is directly proportional to voltage) *[1 mark]*, while the resistance of the lamp increases with current *[1 mark]*.

8 a) clockwise *[1 mark]*
Use Fleming's left-hand rule and remember the magnetic field goes from north to south.

b) A current-carrying wire in a magnetic field experiences a force due to the motor effect *[1 mark]*. The force causes one side of the coil to move upwards and one side to move downwards, causing it to rotate *[1 mark]*.

c) Any two from: e.g. increase the number of turns on the coil *[1 mark]*. / Increase the current in the wire *[1 mark]*. / Increase the magnetic field strength *[1 mark]*.

9 a) $P = \dfrac{F}{A} = \dfrac{25}{0.01} = $ **2500 Pa**

[2 marks for correct answer, otherwise 1 mark for correct substitution.]

b) The force on piston A causes a pressure in the liquid *[1 mark]*. This pressure in the liquid is transmitted equally through the liquid in all directions *[1 mark]*. The pressure of the liquid at piston B causes a force on piston B *[1 mark]*.

c) The pressure on piston B is equal to the pressure on the liquid from piston A: $P_A = P_B$.
So the pressure on piston B = P_B = 2500 Pa
Force on piston B = F_B
$F_B = P_B \times$ Area of piston B = $2500 \times 0.15 = 375\,N$
[2 marks available — 1 mark for stating the pressures on pistons A and B are equal, 1 mark for substituting into the correctly rearranged equation to find the force on piston B.]

10 a) The angle of incidence when a ray hits the outer layer of a fibre is greater than the critical angle *[1 mark]*, so the ray is totally internally reflected and almost none 'escapes' *[1 mark]*.

b) i) E.g. shine a light ray at the block on a piece of paper, at an angle to the block's surface, and trace the block and the incident and emergent rays *[1 mark]*. Remove the block and draw in the refracted ray by connecting the incident and emerging rays. Draw in the normals, and measure the angle of incidence *[1 mark]* and the angle of refraction *[1 mark]* at the air-material boundary. Use the equation
$n = \dfrac{\sin i}{\sin r}$ to calculate the refractive index *[1 mark]*.
You could say lots of other things here. For example, you could say that you'll repeat the experiment for different values of i, or that you'll take several measurements at each value of i.

ii) E.g. laser beams can cause blindness if they shine in your eyes *[1 mark]*, so the student should wear special goggles/ensure that the laser beam is never pointed towards a person/make sure no one stands in front of the laser beam *[1 mark]*.

c) θ = critical angle (c).
$\sin c = \dfrac{1}{n}$ so,
$\theta = \sin^{-1}\left(\dfrac{1}{n}\right) = \sin^{-1}\left(\dfrac{1}{1.5}\right) = 41.81...^\circ$
= **42° (to 2 s.f.)**
[4 marks for correct answer, otherwise 1 mark for stating the equation for sin c, 1 mark for rearranging the equation correctly and 1 mark for correctly substituting into the equation.]

11 a) i) Total distance travelled = total area under the graph.
Splitting it into a rectangle (0-19 s) and a triangle (19-26 s):
Area under the graph = $(19 \times 15) + ((7 \times 15) \div 2)$
= **337.5 m**
[2 marks for the correct answer, otherwise 1 mark for indicating that the distance is represented by the area under the graph and showing working to calculate the area under the entire graph.]

ii) gradient of velocity-time graph = acceleration (/ deceleration)
so acceleration = $\dfrac{\text{change in } y}{\text{change in } x} = \dfrac{0-15}{26-19} = \dfrac{-15}{7}$
= $-2.14285...$ m/s^2
$F = m \times a$
Since the question only asks for the size of the force, you can ignore the minus sign.
So, $F = 1000 \times 2.142... = 2142.85... N = $ **2140 N (to 3 s.f.)**
[4 marks for correct answer, otherwise 1 mark for correct calculation of the gradient of sloped section of v-t graph, 1 mark for equating this to the acceleration, and 1 mark for correct substitution into $F = m \times a$.]
You could also have done this by finding the change in speed from the graph, and using force = change in momentum ÷ time. You'd still get all the marks if you did it correctly this way.

b) i) E.g. at point A when the skydiver first jumps, the downwards force of his weight due to gravity is pulling him down and there are no resistive forces (drag) acting upwards *[1 mark]*. As the skydiver's velocity increases, the resistive forces acting upwards increase *[1 mark]*. When the resistive forces acting upwards balance the force of his weight acting downwards *[1 mark]*, he reaches his terminal velocity and remains at a steady speed until point B *[1 mark]*.

ii) E.g. opening the parachute causes the surface area to increase *[1 mark]*. This causes the resistive forces on the skydiver to increase (while the downwards force of his weight remains unchanged), causing deceleration *[1 mark]*.

12 a) The microwave oven emits microwaves *[1 mark]*. The microwaves penetrate a few centimetres into the food before being absorbed by the water molecules in the food *[1 mark]*. The energy is then conducted or convected to other parts of the food *[1 mark]*.

b) i) speed = frequency × wavelength / $v = f \times \lambda$ *[1 mark]*

ii) $v = f \times \lambda$ so $\lambda = \dfrac{v}{f} = \dfrac{3.0 \times 10^8}{2.5 \times 10^9} = $ **0.12 m**

[2 marks for correct answer, otherwise 1 mark for substituting into the correctly rearranged equation.]

c) i) Some microwaves are absorbed by molecules in the body and can heat human body tissue internally *[1 mark]*. Some people are worried that this might damage health *[1 mark]*.

ii) Radio waves have fewer harmful effects than microwaves because they have a lower frequency *[1 mark]* and so transfer less energy *[1 mark]*.

Practice Paper 2P

1 a) i) D *[1 mark]*

ii) The paint drops all have the same negative charge and so repel each other, forming a fine spray *[1 mark]*. The drops are attracted to the (positively-charged) body panel *[1 mark]*, and so spread out across the panel, including to parts that are not directly facing the spray gun *[1 mark]*.

b) i) E.g. during refuelling, friction causes electrons to be transferred between the fuel and the metal tanker *[1 mark]*. If the tank was made of an insulator, electrons transferred would be unable to move / to be conducted away, and so a charge would build up on the tank *[1 mark]*.

ii) A build-up of charge can cause a spark, and since the fuel and its vapours are flammable, this could cause a fire or explosion *[1 mark]*.

2 a) momentum = mass × velocity / $p = m \times v$ *[1 mark]*

b) Skater A:
$p = m \times v = 70 \times 9.0 = $ **630 kg m/s** *[1 mark]*
Skater B:
$p = m \times v = 50 \times 6.6 = $ **330 kg m/s** *[1 mark]*

c) $p = m \times v \Rightarrow v = \dfrac{p}{m} = \dfrac{630 + 330}{70 + 50} = $ **8 m/s**

[2 marks if answer correct, otherwise 1 mark for correct rearrangement of the equation and correct substitution of values into the equation.]

You'll still get the marks in part c) if either of the answers from part b) you used were wrong, as long as you used the correct method.

d) i) Skater B exerts a force of 100 N in the opposite direction to the original force *[1 mark]*.

ii) (Unbalanced) force = mass × acceleration / $F = m \times a$ *[1 mark]*

iii) $F = m \times a$

$\Rightarrow a = \dfrac{F}{m} = \dfrac{100}{50} = $ **2 m/s² (metres per second squared)**

[3 marks if answer correct, otherwise 1 mark for correct rearrangement of the equation and correct substitution of values into the equation and 1 mark for the correct unit.]

3 a) i) Bio-fuels = 6×10^9 kWh *[1 mark]*
Hydroelectric = 1×10^9 kWh *[1 mark]*

Allow 1 mark only if the answers are 6 kWh and 1 kWh and $\times 10^9$ is omitted

ii) Wind power *[1 mark]*

iii) Any one from: e.g. there are more hours of daylight in summer than in winter, so more electricity can be generated from solar power / there are generally more clear days during summer so more electricity can be generated from solar power *[1 mark]*.

b) Advantage: Any one from: e.g. non-renewables are reliable / we can easily alter energy output to meet demand *[1 mark]*. Disadvantage: Any one from: e.g. non-renewables will eventually run out / burning some non-renewables, e.g. fossil fuels, produces pollutants / burning some non-renewables, e.g. fossil fuels, can cause global warming *[1 mark]*.

c) $100 - 59.2 - 23.9 = $ **16.9%** *[1 mark]*

d) Advantages — any two from: e.g.
The reaction in the nuclear reactor doesn't produce any carbon dioxide emissions (i.e. it doesn't contribute to global warming/air pollution) *[1 mark]*.
There is still a lot of nuclear fuel left in the ground *[1 mark]*.
Nuclear reactions release more energy for the amount of fuel used compared to burning fossil fuels *[1 mark]*.
Disadvantages — any two from: e.g.
It takes longer/costs more to start up nuclear power stations than fossil fuel power stations *[1 mark]*.
There's a risk with nuclear power of leaks of radioactive material or major catastrophe *[1 mark]*.
Radioactive waste from nuclear power stations is very dangerous and difficult to dispose of *[1 mark]*.
Decommissioning nuclear power stations is very expensive *[1 mark]*.

4 a) i) E.g. room temperature/power supplied to heater *[1 mark]*.

ii) Control variables need to be kept constant to make sure that any observed changes are due to just one variable (the independent variable) being changed *[1 mark]*.

b) i)

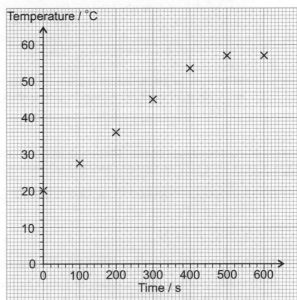

[3 marks — 1 mark for suitable scales chosen (more than half of the graph paper is used), 1 mark for the axes correctly labelled with quantities and units, 1 mark for all the points plotted correctly to within half a square. Deduct 1 mark if 2 or more points are plotted incorrectly.]

ii)

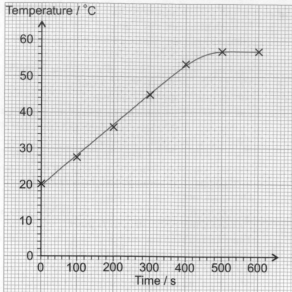

[2 marks — 1 mark for line of best fit drawn straight up to 350 s, 1 mark for line of best fit curving to flat at 500 s.]

c) i) gas *[1 mark]*

ii) C *[1 mark]*

iii) The line is flat because a change of state is occurring *[1 mark]* and all energy transferred to the substance is being used to break intermolecular bonds and change the state of the substance, not increase its temperature *[1 mark]*.

d) i) As temperature increases, the volume of the gas increases / volume is proportional to temperature *[1 mark]*.

ii) Temperature = 25 + 273 = 298 K *[1 mark]*
Reading from the graph, volume at 298 K = **6.1 cm³**
[1 mark, allow for error in calculation of temperature carried forward].

To convert from degrees Celsius to kelvins just add 273. To go from kelvins to Celsius, subtract 273.

5 a) It is a step-up transformer. The voltage increases across it / it has more turns on the secondary coil than the primary coil *[1 mark]*.

b) i) $\dfrac{\text{input (primary) voltage}}{\text{output (secondary) voltage}} = \dfrac{\text{number of turns on primary}}{\text{number of turns on secondary}}$

/ $\dfrac{V_p}{V_s} = \dfrac{N_p}{N_s}$ *[1 mark]*

ii) $\dfrac{V_p}{V_s} = \dfrac{N_p}{N_s} \Rightarrow N_s = \dfrac{N_p \times V_s}{V_p} = \dfrac{5000 \times 400\,000}{25\,000} = \textbf{80\,000 turns}$
[3 marks if answer correct, otherwise 1 mark for correct rearrangement of the equation and 1 mark for correct substitution of values into the equation.]

c) i) input (primary) voltage × input (primary) current = output (secondary) voltage × output (secondary) current /
$V_p I_p = V_s I_s$ *[1 mark]*

ii) $V_p I_p = V_s I_s \Rightarrow I_p = \dfrac{V_s I_s}{V_p} = \dfrac{400\,000 \times 250}{25\,000} = \textbf{4000 A}$
[2 marks if answer correct, otherwise 1 mark for correct rearrangement of the equation and correct substitution of values into the equation.]

d) The electricity produced at power stations has too high a current to be transmitted efficiently. Step-up transformers are needed to increase the voltage and so decrease the current before the electricity is distributed *[1 mark]*. This reduces heating in the wires (the higher the current, the larger the heating effect) *[1 mark]*.

6 a) An electromagnet is a coil of wire connected to a voltage supply which produces a magnetic field when a current flows through it *[1 mark]*.

b) i) E.g.

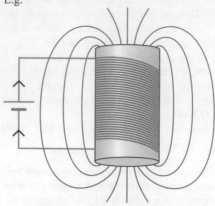

[1 mark]

ii) A magnetically soft core means the core quickly stops being magnetic after the electromagnet is turned off (and so a metal load/object can be dropped) *[1 mark]*.

c) i) moment = force × perpendicular distance from the line of action of the force to the pivot ($M = F \times d$) *[1 mark]*

ii) moment = force × perpendicular distance from the line of action of the force to the pivot
total clockwise moment = 5 × 28 000
total anticlockwise moment = 10 × weight of anvil
total clockwise moment = total anticlockwise moment
So 5 × 28 000 = 10 × weight of anvil
$\Rightarrow$ weight of anvil $= \dfrac{5 \times 28\,000}{10} = \textbf{14\,000 N}$
[3 marks if answer correct, otherwise 1 mark for calculating the clockwise moment and 1 mark for correct rearrangement of the equation and correct substitution of values into the equation.]

7 a) The specific heat capacity of a substance is the energy required to raise the temperature of 1 kg of that substance by 1 °C *[1 mark]*.

b) The results will be more accurate *[1 mark]*, because less of the energy supplied by the coils will be lost from the liquids *[1 mark]*.

c) The change in temperature of a heated substance is dependent on the mass of the substance *[1 mark]*. By keeping both masses the same, any differences in temperature between the two liquids are dependent only on their respective specific heat capacities *[1 mark]*.

d) $\Delta Q = mc\Delta T$
So, $c = \Delta Q \div m\Delta T$
$\Delta T = 93 - 18 = 75$
$c = 126\,000 \div (1 \times 75)$
$= \textbf{1680 J/kg°C}$
[4 marks for correct answer, otherwise 1 mark for correct rearrangement, 1 mark for correct calculation of change in temperature and 1 mark for correct substitution.]

e) Water has a higher specific heat capacity than oil *[1 mark]* so it transfers more energy to the surroundings compared to oil, for the same decrease in temperature *[1 mark]*.

Working Out Your Grade

- Do both exam papers.
- Use the answers and mark scheme to mark each exam paper.
- Use the tables below to record your marks.

Paper 1

Q	Mark	Q	Mark
1		7	
2		8	
3		9	
4		10	
5		11	
6		12	
	Total		/110

Paper 2

Q	Mark	Q	Mark
1		5	
2		6	
3		7	
4			
	Total		/70

- Add together your marks for the two papers to give a total mark out of 180.

Total Mark = Paper 1 Total + Paper 2 Total

Total Mark = ☐ /180

- Look up your total mark in this table to see what grade you got.

Total Mark	Grade
160	9
139	8
118	7
106	6
94	5
82	4
67	3
53	2
38	1
0	U

Important!

The grade boundaries above are given as a guide only.
Exam boards tinker with their boundaries each year, so any grade you get on these practice papers is no guarantee of getting that grade in the real exam — but it should give you a pretty good idea.

Answers

Equations Page

Here are some equations you might find useful when you're doing the practice papers — you'll be given these equations in the real exams.

(final speed)^2 = (initial speed)^2 + (2 × acceleration × distance moved) $v^2 = u^2 + (2 \times a \times s)$	
$\dfrac{\text{energy}}{\text{transferred}}$ = current × voltage × time	$E = I \times V \times t$
frequency = $\dfrac{1}{\text{time period}}$	$f = \dfrac{1}{T}$
power = $\dfrac{\text{work done}}{\text{time taken}}$	$P = \dfrac{W}{t}$
power = $\dfrac{\text{energy transferred}}{\text{time taken}}$	$P = \dfrac{W}{t}$
pressure × volume = constant	$p_1 \times V_1 = p_2 \times V_2$
$\dfrac{\text{pressure}}{\text{temperature}}$ = constant	$\dfrac{p_1}{T_1} = \dfrac{p_2}{T_2}$
orbital speed = $\dfrac{2\pi \times \text{orbital radius}}{\text{time period}}$	$v = \dfrac{2 \times \pi \times r}{T}$

Assume the acceleration due to gravity is g = 10 m/s².

PAPER 2

force = $\dfrac{\text{change in momentum}}{\text{time taken}}$

change in thermal energy = mass × specific heat capacity × change in temperature

$$\Delta Q = m \times c \times \Delta T$$

$\dfrac{\text{change of wavelength}}{\text{wavelength}} = \dfrac{\text{velocity of a galaxy}}{\text{speed of light}}$

$$\frac{\lambda - \lambda_0}{\lambda_0} = \frac{\Delta\lambda}{\lambda_0} = \frac{v}{c}$$

PEQI42